Ruth Hoxie

S0-BJQ-501

THE UNIFORM EDITION OF
THE PLAYS OF J. M. BARRIE

QUALITY STREET

THE WORKS OF J. M. BARRIE.

NOVELS, STORIES, AND SKETCHES.
Uniform Edition.

AULD LICHT IDYLLS, BETTER DEAD.
WHEN A MAN'S SINGLE.
A WINDOW IN THRUMS, AN EDINBURGH
   ELEVEN.
THE LITTLE MINISTER.
SENTIMENTAL TOMMY.
MY LADY NICOTINE, MARGARET OGILVY.
TOMMY AND GRIZEL.
THE LITTLE WHITE BIRD.
PETER AND WENDY.
Also
HALF HOURS, DER TAG.
ECHOES OF WAR.

PLAYS.
Uniform Edition.

A KISS FOR CINDERELLA
ALICE SIT-BY-THE-FIRE.
WHAT EVERY WOMAN KNOWS.
QUALITY STREET.
THE ADMIRABLE CRICHTON.
ECHOES OF THE WAR.
   Containing: THE OLD LADY SHOWS HER
      MEDALS — THE NEW WORD — BAR-
      BARA'S WEDDING — A WELL-REMEM-
      BERED VOICE.

HALF HOURS.
   Containing: PANTALOON—THE TWELVE-
      POUND LOOK—ROSALIND—THE WILL.

Others in Preparation.
INDIVIDUAL EDITIONS.

PETER PAN IN KENSINGTON GARDENS.
   Illustrated by ARTHUR RACKHAM.
PETER AND WENDY.
   Illustrated by F. D. BEDFORD.
TOMMY AND GRIZEL.
   Illustrated by BERNARD PARTRIDGE.
MARGARET OGILVY.

.*. For particulars concerning *The Thistle
Edition* of the Works of J. M. BARRIE, sold only
by subscription, send for circular.

NEW YORK: CHARLES SCRIBNER'S SONS

THE PLAYS OF
J. M. BARRIE

QUALITY STREET

WITHDRAWN

A COMEDY

B10151

PR
4074
Q3

CHARLES SCRIBNER'S SONS

NEW YORK : : : : : : : : : 1921

ST. PAUL
PUBLIC LIBRARY

COPY

COPYRIGHT, 1918, BY
J. M. BARRIE

All rights reserved under the International Copyright Act.
Performance forbidden and right of representation reserved.
Application for the right of performing this play must be
made to Charles Frohman, Inc., Empire Theatre, New York.

GIFT

ST. PAUL
PUBLIC LIBRARY

ACT I

ACT I

THE BLUE AND WHITE ROOM

The scene is the blue and white room in the house of the Misses Susan and Phoebe Throssel in Quality Street; and in this little country town there is a satisfaction about living in Quality Street which even religion cannot give. Through the bowed window at the back we have a glimpse of the street. It is pleasantly broad and grass-grown, and is linked to the outer world by one demure shop, whose door rings a bell every time it opens and shuts. Thus by merely peeping, every one in Quality Street can know at once who has been buying a Whimsy cake, and usually why. This bell is the most familiar sound of Quality Street. Now and again ladies pass in their pattens, a maid perhaps protecting them with an umbrella, for flakes of snow are falling discreetly. Gentlemen in the street are an event; but, see, just as we raise the curtain, there goes the recruiting sergeant to remind us that we are in the period of the Napoleonic wars. If he were to look in at the window of the blue and white room all the ladies there assembled would draw themselves up ; they know him for a rude fellow who smiles at the approach of maiden ladies and continues to smile after they have passed. However, he lowers his head to-day so that they shall not see him, his present design being converse with the Misses Throssel's maid.

The room is one seldom profaned by the foot of man, and everything in it is white or blue. Miss Phoebe is not present, but here are Miss Susan, Miss Willoughby and her sister Miss Fanny, and Miss Henrietta Turnbull. Miss Susan and Miss Willoughby, alas, already wear caps ; but all the four are dear ladies, so refined that we ought not to be discussing them without a more formal introduction. There seems no sufficient reason why we should choose Miss Phoebe as our heroine rather than any one of the others, except, perhaps, that we like her name best. But we gave her the name, so we must support our choice and say that she is slightly the nicest, unless, indeed, Miss Susan is nicer.

Miss Fanny is reading aloud from a library book while the others sew or knit. They are making garments for our brave soldiers now far away fighting the Corsican Ogre.

MISS FANNY. '. . . And so the day passed and evening came, black, mysterious, and ghost-like. The wind moaned unceasingly like a shivering spirit, and the vegetation rustled uneasily as if something weird and terrifying were about to happen. Suddenly out of the darkness there emerged a *Man*.

> (*She says the last word tremulously but without looking up. The listeners knit more quickly.*)

The unhappy Camilla was standing lost in reverie when, without pausing to advertise her of his intentions, he took both her hands in his.

> (*By this time the knitting has stopped, and all are listening as if mesmerised.*)

Slowly he gathered her in his arms——

> (MISS SUSAN *gives an excited little cry.*)

MISS FANNY. And rained hot, burning——'

MISS WILLOUGHBY. Sister !

MISS FANNY (*greedily*). 'On eyes, mouth——'

MISS WILLOUGHBY (*sternly*). Stop. Miss Susan, I am indeed surprised you should bring such an amazing, indelicate tale from the library.

MISS SUSAN (*with a slight shudder*). I deeply regret, Miss Willoughby—— (*Sees* MISS FANNY *reading quickly to herself.*) Oh, Fanny! If you please, my dear.

(*Takes the book gently from her.*)

MISS WILLOUGHBY. I thank you.

(*She knits severely.*)

MISS FANNY (*a little rebel*). Miss Susan is looking at the end.

(MISS SUSAN *closes the book guiltily.*)

MISS SUSAN (*apologetically*). Forgive my partiality for romance, Mary. I fear 'tis the mark of an old maid.

MISS WILLOUGHBY. Susan, that word!

MISS SUSAN (*sweetly*). 'Tis what I am. And you also, Mary, my dear.

MISS FANNY (*defending her sister*). Miss Susan, I protest.

MISS WILLOUGHBY (*sternly truthful*). Nay, sister, 'tis true. We are known everywhere now, Susan, you and I, as the old maids of Quality Street. (*General discomfort.*)

MISS SUSAN. I am happy Phoebe will not be an old maid.

MISS HENRIETTA (*wistfully*). Do you refer, Miss Susan, to V. B. ?

(MISS SUSAN *smiles happily to herself.*)

MISS SUSAN. Miss Phoebe of the ringlets as he has called her.

MISS FANNY. Other females besides Miss Phoebe have ringlets.

MISS SUSAN. But you and Miss Henrietta have to employ papers, my dear. (*Proudly*) Phoebe, never.

MISS WILLOUGHBY (*in defence of* FANNY). I do not approve of Miss Phoebe at all.

MISS SUSAN (*flushing*). Mary, had Phoebe been dying you would have called her an angel, but that is ever the way. 'Tis all jealousy to the bride and good wishes to the corpse. (*Her guests rise, hurt.*) My love, I beg your pardon.

MISS WILLOUGHBY. With your permission, Miss Susan, I shall put on my pattens.

> (MISS SUSAN *gives permission almost haughtily, and the ladies retire to the bedroom,* MISS FANNY *remaining behind a moment to ask a question.*)

MISS FANNY.   A bride?   Miss Susan, do you mean that V. B. has declared?

MISS SUSAN.   Fanny, I expect it hourly.

(MISS SUSAN, *left alone, is agitated by the terrible scene with* MISS WILLOUGHBY.)

(*Enter* PHOEBE *in her bonnet, and we see at once that she really is the nicest. She is so flushed with delightful news that she almost forgets to take off her pattens before crossing the blue and white room.*)

MISS SUSAN.   You seem strangely excited, Phoebe.

PHOEBE.   Susan, I have met a certain individual.

MISS SUSAN.   V. B.?   (PHOEBE *nods several times, and her gleaming eyes tell* MISS SUSAN *as much as if they were a romance from the library.*) My dear, you are trembling.

PHOEBE (*bravely*).   No—oh no.

MISS SUSAN.   You put your hand to your heart.

PHOEBE.   Did I?

MISS SUSAN (*in a whisper*).   My love, has he offered?

PHOEBE (*appalled*).   Oh, Susan.

(*Enter* MISS WILLOUGHBY, *partly cloaked.*)

MISS WILLOUGHBY. How do you do, Miss Phoebe. (*Portentously*) Susan, I have no wish to alarm you, but I am of opinion that there is a man in the house. I suddenly felt it while putting on my pattens.

MISS SUSAN. You mean—a follower—in the kitchen? (*She courageously rings the bell, but her voice falters.*) I am just a little afraid of Patty.

> (*Enter* PATTY, *a buxom young woman, who loves her mistresses and smiles at them, and knows how to terrorise them.*)

Patty, I hope we may not hurt your feelings, but——

PATTY (*sternly*). Are you implicating, ma'am, that I have a follower?

MISS SUSAN. Oh no, Patty.

PATTY. So be it.

MISS SUSAN (*ashamed*). Patty, come back, (*Humbly*) I told a falsehood just now; I am ashamed of myself.

PATTY (*severely*). As well you might be, ma'am.

PHOEBE (*so roused that she would look heroic if*

she did not spoil the effect by wagging her finger at PATTY). How dare you. There is a man in the kitchen. To the door with him.

PATTY. A glorious soldier to be so treated !

PHOEBE. The door.

PATTY. And if he refuses?

    (*They looked perplexed.*)

MISS SUSAN. Oh dear !

PHOEBE. If he refuses send him here to me.

    (*Exit* PATTY.)

MISS SUSAN. Lion-hearted Phoebe.

MISS WILLOUGHBY. A soldier? (*Nervously*) I wish it may not be that impertinent recruiting sergeant. I passed him in the street to-day. He closed one of his eyes at me and then quickly opened it. I knew what he meant.

PHOEBE. He does not come.

MISS SUSAN. I think I hear their voices in dispute.

    (*She is listening through the floor. They all stoop or go on their knees to listen, and when they are in this position the* RECRUITING SERGEANT *enters unobserved. He*

chuckles aloud.　In a moment PHOEBE *is
alone with him.*)

SERGEANT (*with an Irish accent*).　Your
servant, ma'am.

PHOEBE (*advancing sternly on him*).　Sir——
(*She is perplexed, as he seems undismayed.*)
Sergeant—— (*She sees mud from his boots on
the carpet.*)　Oh! oh!　(*Brushes carpet.*)　Sergeant, I am wishful to scold you, but would
you be so obliging as to stand on this paper
while I do it?

SERGEANT.　With all the pleasure in life,
ma'am.

PHOEBE (*forgetting to be angry*).　Sergeant,
have you killed people?

SERGEANT.　Dozens, ma'am, dozens.

PHOEBE.　How terrible.　Oh, sir, I pray
every night that the Lord in His loving-kind-
ness will root the enemy up.　Is it true that
the Corsican Ogre eats babies?

SERGEANT.　I have spoken with them as
have seen him do it, ma'am.

PHOEBE.　The Man of Sin.　Have you ever
seen a vivandiere, sir?　(*Wistfully*) I have

sometimes wished there were vivandieres in the British Army. (*For a moment she sees herself as one.*) Oh, Sergeant, a shudder goes through me when I see you in the streets enticing those poor young men.

SERGEANT. If you were one of them, ma'am, and death or glory was the call, you would take the shilling, ma'am.

PHOEBE. Oh, not for that.

SERGEANT. For King and Country, ma'am?

PHOEBE (*grandly*). Yes, yes, for that.

SERGEANT (*candidly*). Not that it is all fighting. The sack of captured towns—the loot.

PHOEBE (*proudly*). An English soldier never sacks nor loots.

SERGEANT. No, ma'am. And then—the girls.

PHOEBE. What girls?

SERGEANT. In the towns that—that we don't sack.

PHOEBE. How they must hate the haughty conqueror.

SERGEANT. We are not so haughty as all that.

PHOEBE (*sadly*). I think I understand. I am afraid, Sergeant, you do not tell those poor young men the noble things I thought you told them.

SERGEANT. Ma'am, I must e'en tell them what they are wishful to hear. There ha' been five, ma'am, all this week, listening to me and then showing me their heels, but by a grand stroke of luck I have them at last.

PHOEBE. Luck?

> (MISS SUSAN *opens door slightly and listens.*)

SERGEANT. The luck, ma'am, is that a gentleman of the town has enlisted. That gave them the push forward.

> (MISS SUSAN *is excited.*)

PHOEBE. A gentleman of this town enlisted? (*Eagerly*) Sergeant, who?

SERGEANT. Nay, ma'am, I think it be a secret as yet.

PHOEBE. But a gentleman! 'Tis the most amazing, exciting thing. Sergeant, be so obliging.

SERGEANT. Nay, ma'am, I can't.

MISS SUSAN (*at door, carried away by excitement*). But you must, you must!

SERGEANT (*turning to the door*). You see, ma'am——

(*The door is hurriedly closed.*)

PHOEBE (*ashamed*). Sergeant, I have not been saying the things I meant to say to you. Will you please excuse my turning you out of the house somewhat violently.

SERGEANT. I am used to it, ma'am.

PHOEBE. I won't really hurt you.

SERGEANT. Thank you kindly, ma'am.

PHOEBE (*observing the bedroom door opening a little, and speaking in a loud voice*). I protest, sir; we shall permit no followers in this house. Should I discover you in my kitchen again I shall pitch you out—neck and crop. Begone, sir.

(*The* SERGEANT *retires affably. All the ladies except* MISS HENRIETTA *come out, admiring* PHOEBE. *The* WILLOUGHBYS *are attired for their journey across the street.*)

MISS WILLOUGHBY. Miss Phoebe, we could not but admire you.

(PHOEBE, *alas, knows that she is not admirable.*)

PHOEBE. But the gentleman recruit?

MISS SUSAN. Perhaps they will know who he is at the woollen-drapers.

MISS FANNY. Let us inquire.

(*But before they go* MISS WILLOUGHBY *has a duty to perform.*)

MISS WILLOUGHBY. I wish to apologise. Miss Phoebe, you are a dear, good girl. If I have made remarks about her ringlets, Susan, it was jealousy. (PHOEBE *and* MISS SUSAN *wish to embrace her, but she is not in the mood for it.*) Come, sister.

MISS FANNY (*the dear woman that she is*). Phoebe, dear, I wish you very happy.

(PHOEBE *presses her hand.*)

MISS HENRIETTA (*entering, and not to be outdone*). Miss Phoebe, I give you joy.

(*The three ladies go, the two younger ones a little tearfully, and we see them pass the window.*)

PHOEBE (*pained*). Susan, you have been talking to them about V. B.

MISS SUSAN. I could not help it. (*Eagerly*) Now, Phoebe, what is it you have to tell me?

PHOEBE (*in a low voice*). Dear, I think it is too holy to speak of.

MISS SUSAN. To your sister?

PHOEBE. Susan, as you know, I was sitting with an unhappy woman whose husband has fallen in the war. When I came out of the cottage *he* was passing.

MISS SUSAN. Yes?

PHOEBE. He offered me his escort. At first he was very silent—as he has often been of late.

MISS SUSAN. *We* know why.

PHOEBE. Please not to say that I know why. Suddenly he stopped and swung his cane. You know how gallantly he swings his cane.

MISS SUSAN. Yes, indeed.

PHOEBE. He said: 'I have something I am wishful to tell you, Miss Phoebe; perhaps you can guess what it is.'

MISS SUSAN. Go on!

PHOEBE. To say I could guess, sister, would have been unladylike. I said: 'Please not to tell me in the public thoroughfare'; to which he instantly replied: 'Then I shall call and tell you this afternoon.'

MISS SUSAN.   Phoebe!

(*They are interrupted by the entrance of* PATTY *with tea. They see that she has brought three cups, and know that this is her impertinent way of implying that mistresses, as well as maids, may have a 'follower.' When she has gone they smile at the daring of the woman, and sit down to tea.*)

PHOEBE.   Susan, to think that it has all happened in a single year.

MISS SUSAN.   Such a genteel competency as he can offer; such a desirable establishment.

PHOEBE.   I had no thought of that, dear.   I was recalling our first meeting at Mrs. Fotheringay's quadrille party.

MISS SUSAN.   We had quite forgotten that our respected local physician was growing elderly.

PHOEBE.   Until he said: 'Allow me to present my new partner, Mr. Valentine Brown.'

MISS SUSAN.   Phoebe, do you remember how

at the tea-table he facetiously passed the cake-basket with nothing in it!

PHOEBE. He was so amusing from the first. I am thankful, Susan, that I too have a sense of humour. I am exceedingly funny at times; am I not, Susan?

MISS SUSAN. Yes, indeed. But he sees humour in the most unexpected things. I say something so ordinary about loving, for instance, to have everything either blue or white in this room, and I know not why he laughs, but it makes me feel quite witty.

PHOEBE (*a little anxiously*). I hope he sees nothing odd or quaint about us.

MISS SUSAN. My dear, I am sure he cannot.

PHOEBE. Susan, the picnics.

MISS SUSAN. Phoebe, the day when he first drank tea in this house.

PHOEBE. He invited himself.

MISS SUSAN. He merely laughed when I said it would cause such talk.

PHOEBE. He is absolutely fearless. Susan, he has smoked his pipe in this room.

(*They are both a little scared.*)

MISS SUSAN.   Smoking is indeed a dreadful habit.

PHOEBE.   But there is something so dashing about it.

MISS SUSAN (*with melancholy*).   And now I am to be left alone.

PHOEBE.   No.

MISS SUSAN.   My dear, I could not leave this room.   My lovely blue and white room.   It is my husband.

PHOEBE (*who has become agitated*).   Susan, you must make my house your home.   I have something distressing to tell you.

MISS SUSAN.   You alarm me.

PHOEBE.   You know Mr. Brown advised us how to invest half of our money.

MISS SUSAN.   I know it gives us eight per cent., though why it should do so I cannot understand, but very obliging, I am sure.

PHOEBE.   Susan, all that money is lost; I had the letter several days ago.

MISS SUSAN.   Lost?

PHOEBE.   Something burst, dear, and then they absconded.

MISS SUSAN. But Mr. Brown——

PHOEBE. I have not advertised him of it yet, for he will think it was his fault. But I shall tell him to-day.

MISS SUSAN. Phoebe, how much have we left?

PHOEBE. Only sixty pounds a year, so you see you must live with us, dearest.

MISS SUSAN. But Mr. Brown—he——

PHOEBE (*grandly*). He is a man of means, and if he is not proud to have my Susan I shall say at once: 'Mr. Brown—the door.'

(*She presses her cheek to* MISS SUSAN's.)

MISS SUSAN (*softly*). Phoebe, I have a wedding gift for you.

PHOEBE. Not yet?

MISS SUSAN. It has been ready for a long time. I began it when you were not ten years old and I was a young woman. I meant it for myself, Phoebe. I had hoped that he—his name was William—but I think I must have been too unattractive, my love.

PHOEBE. Sweetest—dearest——

MISS SUSAN. I always associate it with a sprigged poplin I was wearing that summer,

with a breadth of coloured silk in it, being a
naval officer; but something happened, a Miss
Cicely Pemberton, and they are quite big boys
now. So long ago, Phoebe—he was very tall,
with brown hair—it was most foolish of
me, but I was always so fond of sewing—
with long straight legs and such a pleasant
expression.

PHOEBE. Susan, what was it?

MISS SUSAN. It was a wedding-gown, my
dear. Even plain women, Phoebe, we can't
help it; when we are young we have romantic
ideas just as if we were pretty. And so the
wedding-gown was never used. Long before it
was finished I knew he would not offer, but I
finished it, and then I put it away. I have
always hidden it from you, Phoebe, but of late
I have brought it out again, and altered it.

(*She goes to ottoman and unlocks it.*)

PHOEBE. Susan, I could not wear it. (MISS
SUSAN *brings the wedding-gown.*) Oh! how
sweet, how beautiful!

MISS SUSAN. You will wear it, my love,
won't you? And the tears it was sewn with

long ago will all turn into smiles on my Phoebe's wedding-day.

> (*They are tearfully happy when a knock is heard on the street door.*)

PHOEBE. That knock.

MISS SUSAN. So dashing.

PHOEBE. So imperious. (*She is suddenly panic-stricken.*) Susan, I think he kissed me once.

MISS SUSAN (*startled*). You *think*?

PHOEBE. I know he did. That evening— a week ago, when he was squiring me home from the concert. It was raining, and my face was wet; he said that was why he did it.

MISS SUSAN. Because your face was wet?

PHOEBE. It does not seem a sufficient excuse now.

MISS SUSAN (*appalled*). O Phoebe, before he had offered.

PHOEBE (*in distress*). I fear me it was most unladylike.

> (VALENTINE BROWN *is shown in. He is a frank, genial young man of twenty-five who honestly admires the ladies, though he is amused by their quaintness. He is*

*modestly aware that it is in the blue and
white room alone that he is esteemed a wit.*)

BROWN.   Miss Susan, how do you do, ma'am?
Nay, Miss Phoebe, though we have met to-day
already I insist on shaking hands with you again.

MISS SUSAN.   Always so dashing.

(VALENTINE *laughs and the ladies exchange
delighted smiles.*)

VALENTINE (*to* MISS SUSAN).   And my other
friends, I hope I find them in health?   The
spinet, ma'am, seems quite herself to-day; I
trust the ottoman passed a good night?

MISS SUSAN (*beaming*).   We are all quite well,
sir.

VALENTINE.   May I sit on this chair, Miss
Phoebe?   I know Miss Susan likes me to break
her chairs.

MISS SUSAN.   Indeed, sir, I do not.   Phoebe,
how strange that he should think so.

PHOEBE (*instantly*).   The remark was humor-
ous, was it not?

VALENTINE.   How you see through me, Miss
Phoebe.

(*The   sisters   again   exchange   delighted*

smiles. VALENTINE *is about to take a seat.*)

MISS SUSAN (*thinking aloud*). Oh dear, I feel sure he is going to roll the coverlet into a ball and then sit on it.

(VALENTINE, *who has been on the point of doing so, abstains and sits guiltily.*)

VALENTINE. So I am dashing, Miss Susan? Am I dashing, Miss Phoebe?

PHOEBE. A—little, I think.

VALENTINE. Well, but I have something to tell you to-day which I really think is rather dashing. (MISS SUSAN *gathers her knitting, looks at* PHOEBE, *and is preparing to go.*) You are not going, ma'am, before you know what it is?

MISS SUSAN. I—I—indeed—to be sure—I—I know, Mr. Brown.

PHOEBE. Susan!

MISS SUSAN. I mean I do not know. I mean I can guess—I mean—— Phoebe, my love, explain. (*She goes out.*)

VALENTINE (*rather disappointed*). The explanation being, I suppose, that you both know, and I had flattered myself 'twas such a secret.

Am I then to understand that you had foreseen
it all, Miss Phoebe?

PHOEBE.   Nay, sir, you must not ask that.

VALENTINE.   I believe in any case 'twas you
who first put it into my head.

PHOEBE (*aghast*).   Oh, I hope not.

VALENTINE.   Your demure eyes flashed so
every time the war was mentioned; the little
Quaker suddenly looked like a gallant boy in
ringlets.

> (*A dread comes over* PHOEBE, *but it is
> in her heart alone ; it shows neither in
> face nor voice.*)

PHOEBE.   Mr. Brown, what is it you have to
tell us?

VALENTINE.   That I have enlisted, Miss
Phoebe. Did you surmise it was something else?

PHOEBE.   You are going to the wars?   Mr.
Brown, is it a jest?

VALENTINE.   It would be a sorry jest, ma'am.
I thought you knew. I concluded that the
recruiting sergeant had talked.

PHOEBE.   The recruiting sergeant?   I see.

VALENTINE.   These   stirring   times,   Miss

Phoebe—he is but half a man who stays at
home.   I have chafed for months.   I want to
see whether I have any courage, and as to be
an army surgeon does not appeal to me, it was
enlist or remain behind.   To-day I found that
there were five waverers.   I asked them would
they take the shilling if I took it, and they
assented.   Miss Phoebe, it is not one man I give
to the King, but six.

PHOEBE (*brightly*).   I think you have done
bravely.

VALENTINE.   We leave shortly for the Peters-
burgh barracks, and I go to London to-
morrow; so this is good-bye.

PHOEBE.   I shall pray that you may be
preserved in battle, Mr. Brown.

VALENTINE.   And you and Miss Susan will
write to me when occasion offers?

PHOEBE.   If you wish it.

VALENTINE (*smiling*).   With all the stirring
news of Quality Street.

PHOEBE.   It seems stirring to us; it must
have been merely laughable to you, who came
here from a great city.

VALENTINE.   Dear   Quality   Street—that
thought me dashing !   But I made friends in it,
Miss Phoebe, of two very sweet ladies.

PHOEBE (*timidly*).   Mr. Brown, I wonder
why you have been so kind to my sister and
me?

VALENTINE.   The kindness was yours.   If at
first Miss Susan amused me——   (*Chuckling.*)
To see her on her knees decorating the little legs
of the couch with frills as if it were a child !
But it was her sterling qualities that impressed
me presently.

PHOEBE.   And did—did I amuse you also?

VALENTINE.   Prodigiously,   Miss   Phoebe.
Those other ladies, they were always scolding
you, your youthfulness shocked them.   I believe
they thought you dashing.

PHOEBE (*nervously*).   I have sometimes feared
that I was perhaps too dashing.

VALENTINE (*laughing at this*).   You delicious
Miss Phoebe.   You were too quiet.   I felt sorry
that one so sweet and young should live so
grey a life.   I wondered whether I could put
any little pleasures into it.

PHOEBE.   The picnics?   It was very good of you.

VALENTINE.   That was only how it began, for soon I knew that it was I who got the pleasures and you who gave them.   You have been to me, Miss Phoebe, like a quiet, old-fashioned garden full of the flowers that Englishmen love best because they have known them longest: the daisy, that stands for innocence, and the hyacinth for constancy, and the modest violet and the rose.   When I am far away, ma'am, I shall often think of Miss Phoebe's pretty soul, which is her garden, and shut my eyes and walk in it.

(*She is smiling gallantly through her pain when* MISS SUSAN *returns.*)

MISS SUSAN.   Have you—is it—you seem so calm, Phoebe.

PHOEBE (*pressing her sister's hand warningly and imploringly*).   Susan, what Mr. Brown is so obliging as to inform us of is not what we expected—not that at all.   My dear, he is the gentleman who has enlisted, and he came to tell us that and to say good-bye.

MISS SUSAN. Going away?

PHOEBE. Yes, dear.

VALENTINE. Am I not the ideal recruit, ma'am: a man without a wife or a mother or a sweetheart?

MISS SUSAN. No sweetheart?

VALENTINE. Have you one for me, Miss Susan?

PHOEBE (*hastily, lest her sister's face should betray the truth*). Susan, we shall have to tell him now. You dreadful man, you will laugh and say it is just like Quality Street. But indeed since I met you to-day and you told me you had something to communicate we have been puzzling what it could be, and we concluded that you were going to be married.

VALENTINE. Ha! ha! ha! Was that it.

PHOEBE. So like women, you know. We thought we perhaps knew her. (*Glancing at the wedding-gown.*) We were even discussing what we should wear at the wedding.

VALENTINE. Ha! ha! I shall often think of this. I wonder who would have me, Miss

Susan. *(Rising.)* But I must be off; and God bless you both.

MISS SUSAN *(forlorn).* You are going!

VALENTINE. No more mud on your carpet, Miss Susan; no more coverlets rolled into balls. A good riddance. Miss Phoebe, a last look at the garden.

(Taking her hand and looking into her face.)

PHOEBE. We shall miss you very much, Mr. Brown.

VALENTINE. There is one little matter. That investment I advised you to make, I am happy it has turned out so well.

PHOEBE *(checking MISS SUSAN, who is about to tell of the loss of the money).* It was good of you to take all that trouble, sir. Accept our grateful thanks.

VALENTINE. Indeed I am glad that you are so comfortably left; I am your big brother. Good-bye again. *(Looks round.)* This little blue and white room and its dear inmates, may they be unchanged when I come back. Good-bye.

(He goes. MISS SUSAN looks forlornly at PHOEBE, who smiles pitifully.)

PHOEBE. A misunderstanding; just a mistake. (*She shudders, lifts the wedding-gown and puts it back in the ottoman.* MISS SUSAN *sinks sobbing into a chair.*) Don't, dear, don't—we can live it down.

MISS SUSAN (*fiercely*). He is a fiend in human form.

PHOEBE. Nay, you hurt me, sister. He is a brave gentleman.

MISS SUSAN. The money; why did you not let me tell him?

PHOEBE (*flushing*). So that he might offer to me out of pity, Susan?

MISS SUSAN. Phoebe, how are we to live with the quartern loaf at one and tenpence?

PHOEBE. Brother James——

MISS SUSAN. You know very well that brother James will do nothing for us.

PHOEBE. I think, Susan, we could keep a little school—for genteel children only, of course. I would do most of the teaching.

MISS SUSAN. You a schoolmistress—Phoebe of the ringlets; every one would laugh.

PHOEBE. I shall hide the ringlets away in a

cap like yours, Susan, and people will soon forget them. And I shall try to look staid and to grow old quickly. It will not be so hard to me as you think, dear.

MISS SUSAN. There were other gentlemen who were attracted by you, Phoebe, and you turned from them.

PHOEBE. I did not want them.

MISS SUSAN. They will come again, and others.

PHOEBE. No, dear; never speak of that to me any more. (*In woe.*) I let him kiss me.

MISS SUSAN. You could not prevent him.

PHOEBE. Yes, I could. I know I could now. I wanted him to do it. Oh, never speak to me of others after that. Perhaps he saw I wanted it and did it to please me. But I meant —indeed I did—that I gave it to him with all my love. Sister, I could bear all the rest; but I have been unladylike.

> (*The curtain falls, and we do not see the sisters again for ten years.*)

End of Act I.

ACT II

ACT II

THE SCHOOL

Ten years later. It is the blue and white room still, but many of Miss Susan's beautiful things have gone, some of them never to return ; others are stored upstairs. Their place is taken by grim schol-astic furniture : forms, a desk, a globe, a blackboard, heartless maps. It is here that Miss Phoebe keeps school. Miss Susan teaches in the room opening off it, once the spare bedroom, where there is a smaller blackboard (for easier sums) but no globe, as Miss Susan is easily alarmed. Here are the younger pupils unless they have grown defiant, when they are promoted to the blue and white room to be under Miss Phoebe's braver rule. They really frighten Miss Phoebe also, but she does not let her sister know this.

It is noon on a day in August, and through the window we can see that Quality Street is decorated with flags. We also hear at times martial music from another street. Miss Phoebe is giving a dancing lesson to half a dozen pupils, and is doing her very best ;

35

*now she is at the spinet while they dance, and again
she is showing them the new step. We know it is Miss
Phoebe because some of her pretty airs and graces still
cling to her in a forlorn way, but she is much changed.
Her curls are out of sight under a cap, her manner is
prim, the light has gone from her eyes and buoyancy
from her figure; she looks not ten years older but
twenty, and not an easy twenty. When the children
are not looking at her we know that she has the headache.*

PHOEBE (*who is sometimes at the spinet and
sometimes dancing*). Toes out. So. Chest out.
Georgy. Point your toes, Miss Beveridge—so.
So—keep in line; and young ladies, remember
your toes. (GEORGY *in his desire to please has
protruded the wrong part of his person. She
writes a C on his chest with chalk.*) C stands for
chest, Georgy. This is S.

> (MISS SUSAN *darts out of the other room.
> She is less worn than* MISS PHOEBE.)

MISS SUSAN (*whispering so that the pupils may
not hear*). Phoebe, how many are fourteen and
seventeen?

PHOEBE (*almost instantly*). Thirty-one.

MISS SUSAN.   I thank you.   (*She darts off.*)

PHOEBE.   That will do, ladies and gentlemen.
You may go.

> (*They bow or curtsy, and retire to* MISS
> SUSAN'S *room, with the exception of*
> ARTHUR WELLESLEY TOMSON, *who is
> standing in disgrace in a corner with the
> cap of shame on his head, and* ISABELLA,
> *a forbidding-looking, learned little girl.*
> ISABELLA *holds up her hand for permis-
> sion to speak.*)

ISABELLA.   Please, ma'am, father wishes me
to acquire algebra.

PHOEBE (*with a sinking*).   Algebra !   It—it
is not a very ladylike study, Isabella.

ISABELLA.   Father says, will you or won't
you?

PHOEBE.   And you are thin.   It will make
you thinner, my dear.

ISABELLA.   Father says I am thin but wiry.

PHOEBE.   Yes, you are.   (*With feeling.*) You
are very wiry, Isabella.

ISABELLA.   Father says, either I acquire
algebra or I go to Miss Prothero's establishment.

PHOEBE. Very well, I—I will do my best. You may go.

(ISABELLA *goes and* PHOEBE *sits wearily.*)

ARTHUR (*fingering his cap*). Please, ma'am, may I take it off now?

PHOEBE. Certainly not. Unhappy boy—— (ARTHUR *grins.*) Come here. Are you ashamed of yourself?

ARTHUR (*blithely*). No, ma'am.

PHOEBE (*in a terrible voice*). Arthur Wellesley Tomson, fetch me the implement. (ARTHUR *goes briskly for the cane, and she hits the desk with it.*) Arthur, surely that terrifies you?

ARTHUR. No, ma'am.

PHOEBE. Arthur, why did you fight with that street boy?

ARTHUR. 'Cos he said that when you caned you did not draw blood.

PHOEBE. But I don't, do I?

ARTHUR. No, ma'am.

PHOEBE. Then why fight him? (*Remembering how strange boys are.*) Was it for the honour of the school?

ARTHUR. Yes, ma'am.

PHOEBE. Say you are sorry, Arthur, and I won't punish you.

(*He bursts into tears.*)

ARTHUR. You promised to cane me, and now you are not going to do it.

PHOEBE (*incredulous*). Do you *wish* to be caned?

ARTHUR (*holding out his hand eagerly*). If you please, Miss Phoebe.

PHOEBE. Unnatural boy. (*She canes him in a very unprofessional manner.*) Poor dear boy.

(*She kisses the hand.*)

ARTHUR (*gloomily*). Oh, ma'am, you will never be able to cane if you hold it like that. You should hold it like this, Miss Phoebe, and give it a wriggle like that.

(*She is too soft-hearted to follow his instructions.*)

PHOEBE (*almost in tears*). Go away.

ARTHUR (*remembering that women are strange*). Don't cry, ma'am; I love you, Miss Phoebe.

(*She seats him on her knee, and he thinks of a way to please her.*)

If any boy says you can't cane I will blood him, Miss Phoebe.

> (PHOEBE *shudders, and* MISS SUSAN *again darts in. She signs to* PHOEBE *to send* ARTHUR *away.*)

MISS SUSAN (*as soon as* ARTHUR *has gone*). Phoebe, if a herring and a half cost three ha'pence, how many for elevenpence?

PHOEBE (*instantly*). Eleven.

MISS SUSAN. William Smith says it is fifteen; and he is such a big boy, do you think I ought to contradict him? May I say there are differences of opinion about it? No one can be really sure, Phoebe.

PHOEBE. It is eleven. I once worked it out with real herrings. (*Stoutly.*) Susan, we must never let the big boys know that we are afraid of them. To awe them, stamp with the foot, speak in a ferocious voice, and look them unflinchingly in the face. (*Then she pales.*) Oh, Susan, Isabella's father insists on her acquiring algebra.

MISS SUSAN. What is algebra exactly; is it those three cornered things?

PHOEBE. It is x minus y equals z plus y and

things like that. And all the time you are
saying they are equal, you feel in your heart,
why should they be.

> (*The music of the band swells here, and
> both ladies put their hands to their ears.*)

It is the band for to-night's ball. We must
not grudge their rejoicings, Susan. It is not
every year that there is a Waterloo to celebrate.

MISS SUSAN. I was not thinking of that. I
was thinking that *he* is to be at the ball to-night;
and we have not seen him for ten years.

PHOEBE (*calmly*). Yes, ten years. We shall
be glad to welcome our old friend back, Susan.
I am going in to your room now to take the
Latin class.

> (*A soldier with a girl passes—a yokel
> follows angrily.*)

MISS SUSAN. Oh, that weary Latin, I wish I
had the whipping of the man who invented it.

> (*She returns to her room, and the sound of
> the music dies away.* MISS PHOEBE, *who is
> not a very accomplished classical scholar,
> is taking a final peep at the declensions
> when* MISS SUSAN *reappears excitedly.*)

PHOEBE.   What is it?

MISS SUSAN (*tragically*).   William Smith!
Phoebe, I tried to look ferocious, indeed I did,
but he saw I was afraid, and before the whole
school he put out his tongue at me.

PHOEBE.   Susan!

> (*She is lion-hearted; she remembers*
> ARTHUR'S *instructions, and practises with
> the cane.*)

MISS SUSAN (*frightened*).   Phoebe, he is much
too big.   Let it pass.

PHOEBE.   If I let it pass I am a stumbling-
block in the way of true education.

MISS SUSAN.   Sister.

PHOEBE (*grandly*).   Susan, stand aside.

> (*Giving the cane* ARTHUR'S *most telling
> flick, she marches into the other room.
> Then, while* MISS SUSAN *is listening
> nervously,* CAPTAIN VALENTINE BROWN *is
> ushered in by* PATTY.   *He is bronzed and
> soldierly.   He wears the whiskers of the
> period, and is in uniform.   He has lost his
> left hand, but this is not at first noticeable.*)

PATTY.   Miss Susan, 'tis Captain Brown!

MISS SUSAN.   Captain Brown!

VALENTINE (*greeting her warmly*).   Reports himself at home again.

MISS SUSAN (*gratified*).   You call this home?

VALENTINE.   When the other men talked of their homes, Miss Susan, I thought of this room. (*Looking about him.*)   Maps—desks—heigho! But still it is the same dear room.   I have often dreamt, Miss Susan, that I came back to it in muddy shoes.   (*Seeing her alarm.*)   I have not, you know!   Miss Susan, I rejoice to find no change in you; and Miss Phoebe—Miss Phoebe of the ringlets—I hope there be as little change in her?

MISS SUSAN (*painfully*).   Phoebe of the ringlets!   Ah, Captain Brown, you need not expect to see her.

VALENTINE.   She is not here?   I vow it spoils all my home-coming.

> (*At this moment the door of the other room is flung open and* PHOEBE *rushes out, followed by* WILLIAM SMITH *who is brandishing the cane.* VALENTINE *takes in the situation, and without looking at*

PHOEBE *seizes* WILLIAM *by the collar and marches him out of the school.*)

MISS SUSAN.   Phoebe, did you see who it is?

PHOEBE.   I saw.   (*In a sudden tremor.*) Susan, I have lost all my looks.

(*The pupils are crowding in from* MISS SUSAN'S *room and she orders them back and goes with them.* VALENTINE *returns, and speaks as he enters, not recognising* PHOEBE, *whose back is to him.*)

VALENTINE.   A young reprobate, madam, but I have deposited him on the causeway.   I fear—

(*He stops, puzzled because the lady has covered her face with her hands.*)

PHOEBE.   Captain Brown.

VALENTINE.   Miss Phoebe, it is you?

(*He goes to her, but he cannot help show- ing that her appearance is a shock to him.*)

PHOEBE (*without bitterness*).   Yes, I have changed very much, I have not worn well, Captain Brown.

VALENTINE (*awkwardly*).   We—we are both older, Miss Phoebe.

(*He holds out his hand warmly, with affected high spirits.*)

PHOEBE (*smiling reproachfully*).   It was both hands when you went away.   (*He has to show that his left hand is gone ; she is overcome.*)   I did not know.   (*She presses the empty sleeve in remorse.*)   You never mentioned it in your letters.

VALENTINE (*now grown rather stern*).   Miss Phoebe, what did *you* omit from your letters that you had such young blackguards as that to terrify you?

PHOEBE.   He is the only one.   Most of them are dear children; and this is the last day of the term.

VALENTINE.   Ah, ma'am, if only you had invested all your money as you laid out part by my advice.   What a monstrous pity you did not.

PHOEBE.   We never thought of it.

VALENTINE.   You look so tired.

PHOEBE.   I have the headache to-day.

VALENTINE.   You did not use to have the headache.   Curse those dear children.

PHOEBE (*bravely*). Nay, do not distress yourself about me. Tell me of yourself. We are so
proud of the way in which you won your com-
mission. Will you leave the army now?

VALENTINE. Yes; and I have some intention
of pursuing again the old life in Quality Street.
(*He is not a man who has reflected much. He has
come back thinking that all the adventures have
been his, and that the old life in Quality Street has
waited, as in a sleep, to be resumed on the day of
his return.*) I came here in such high spirits,
Miss Phoebe.

PHOEBE (*with a wry smile*). The change in me
depresses you.

VALENTINE. I was in hopes that you and Miss
Susan would be going to the ball. I had brought
cards for you with me to make sure.

> (*She is pleased and means to accept. He
> sighs, and she understands that he thinks
> her too old.*)

PHOEBE. But now you see that my dancing
days are done.

VALENTINE (*uncomfortably*). Ah, no.

PHOEBE (*taking care he shall not see that he has*

hurt her).   But you will find many charming partners.   Some of them have been my pupils. There was even a pupil of mine who fought at Waterloo.

VALENTINE.   Young Blades; I have heard him on it.   (*She puts her hand wearily to her head*).   Miss Phoebe—what a dull grey world it is!

> (*She turns away to hide her emotion, and* MISS SUSAN *comes in.*)

MISS SUSAN.   Phoebe, I have said that you will not take the Latin class to-day, and I am dismissing them.

VALENTINE.   Latin?

PHOEBE (*rather defiantly*).   I am proud to teach it.   (*Breaking down.*)   Susan—his arm— have you seen?

> (MISS SUSAN *also is overcome, but recovers as the children crowd in.*)

MISS SUSAN.   Hats off, gentlemen salute, ladies curtsy—to the brave Captain Brown.

> (CAPTAIN BROWN *salutes them awkwardly, and they cheer him, to his great discomfort, as they pass out.*)

VALENTINE (*when they have gone*).   A terrible ordeal, ma'am.

> (*The old friends look at each other, and there is a silence.* VALENTINE *feels that all the fine tales and merry jests he has brought back for the ladies have turned into dead things. He wants to go away and think.*)

PHOEBE.   I wish you very happy at the ball.

VALENTINE (*sighing*).   Miss Susan, cannot we turn all these maps and horrors out till the vacation is over?

MISS SUSAN.   Indeed, sir, we always do.   By to-morrow this will be my dear blue and white room again, and that my sweet spare bed-room.

PHOEBE.   For five weeks!

VALENTINE (*making vain belief*).   And then— the—the dashing Mr. Brown will drop in as of old, and, behold, Miss Susan on her knees once more putting tucks into my little friend the ottoman, and Miss Phoebe—Miss Phoebe——

PHOEBE.   Phoebe of the ringlets!

> (*She goes out quietly.*)

VALENTINE (*miserably*).   Miss Susan, what a shame it is.

MISS SUSAN (*hotly*).   Yes, it is a shame.

VALENTINE (*suddenly become more of a man*). The brave Captain Brown !   Good God, ma'am, how much more brave are the ladies who keep a school.

> (PATTY *shows in two visitors,* MISS CHARLOTTE PARRATT *and* ENSIGN BLADES. CHARLOTTE *is a pretty minx who we are glad to say does not reside in Quality Street, and* BLADES *is a callow youth, inviting admiration.*)

CHARLOTTE (*as they salute*).   But I did not know you had company, Miss Susan.

MISS SUSAN.   'Tis Captain Brown—Miss Charlotte Parratt.

CHARLOTTE (*gushing*).   The heroic Brown ?

VALENTINE.   Alas, no, ma'am, the other one.

CHARLOTTE.   Miss Susan, do you see who accompanies me ?

MISS SUSAN.   I cannot quite recall——

BLADES.   A few years ago, ma'am, there sat

in this room a scrubby, inky little boy—I was that boy.

MISS SUSAN.   Can it be our old pupil—Ensign Blades?

> (*She thinks him very fine, and he bows, well pleased.*)

BLADES.   Once a little boy and now your most obedient, ma'am.

MISS SUSAN.   You have come to recall old memories?

BLADES.   Not   precisely;   I—Charlotte, explain.

CHARLOTTE.   Ensign Blades wishes me to say that it must seem highly romantic to you to have had a pupil who has fought at Waterloo.

MISS SUSAN.   Not exactly *romantic*.   I trust, sir, that when you speak of having been our pupil you are also so obliging as to mention that it was during our first year.   Otherwise it makes us seem so elderly.

> (*He bows again, in what he believes to be a quizzical manner.*)

CHARLOTTE.   Ensign Blades would be pleased

ST PAUL
PUBLIC LIBRARY

to hear, Miss Susan, what you think of him as a whole.

MISS SUSAN. Indeed, sir, I think you are monstrous fine. (*Innocently.*) It quite awes me to remember that we used to whip him.

VALENTINE (*delighted*). Whipped him, Miss Susan! (*In solemn burlesque of* CHARLOTTE.) Ensign Blades wishes to indicate that it was more than Buonaparte could do. We shall meet again, bright boy.

(*He makes his adieux and goes.*)

BLADES. Do you think he was quizzing me?

MISS SUSAN (*simply*). I cannot think so.

BLADES. He said 'bright boy,' ma'am.

MISS SUSAN. I am sure, sir, he did not mean it.

(PHOEBE *returns.*)

PHOEBE. Charlotte, I am happy to see you. You look delicious, my dear—so young and fresh.

CHARLOTTE. La! Do you think so, Miss Phoebe?

BLADES. Miss Phoebe, your obedient.

PHOEBE. It is Ensign Blades! But how kind of you, sir, to revisit the old school. Please to sit down.

CHARLOTTE. Ensign Blades has a favour to ask of you, Miss Phoebe.

BLADES. I learn, ma'am, that Captain Brown has obtained a card for you for the ball, and I am here to solicit for the honour of standing up with you.

> (*For the moment* PHOEBE *is flattered. Here, she believes, is some one who does not think her too old for the dance. Then she perceives a meaning smile pass between* CHARLOTTE *and the* ENSIGN.)

PHOEBE (*paling*). Is it that you desire to make sport of me?

BLADES (*honestly distressed*). Oh no, ma'am, I vow—but I—I am such a quiz, ma'am.

MISS SUSAN. Sister!

PHOEBE. I am sorry, sir, to have to deprive you of some entertainment, but I am not going to the ball.

MISS SUSAN (*haughtily*). Ensign Blades, I bid you my adieux.

BLADES (*ashamed*). If I have hurt Miss Phoebe's feelings I beg to apologise.

MISS SUSAN. *If* you have hurt them. Oh, sir, how is it possible for any one to be as silly as you seem to be.

BLADES (*who cannot find the answer*). Charlotte —explain.

> (*But* CHARLOTTE *considers that their visit has not been sufficiently esteemed and departs with a cold curtsy, taking him with her.*)
>
> (MISS SUSAN *turns sympathetically to* PHOEBE, *but* PHOEBE, *fighting with her pain, sits down at the spinet and plays at first excitedly a gay tune, then slowly, then comes to a stop with her head bowed. Soon she jumps up courageously, brushes away her distress, gets an algebra book from the desk and sits down to study it.* MISS SUSAN *is at the window, where ladies and gentlemen are now seen passing in ball attire.*)

MISS SUSAN.   What book is it, Phoebe?

PHOEBE.   It is an algebra.

MISS SUSAN. They are going by to the ball. (*In anger.*) My Phoebe should be going to the ball, too.

PHOEBE. You jest, Susan. (MISS SUSAN *watches her read.* PHOEBE *has to wipe away a tear; soon she rises and gives way to the emotion she has been suppressing ever since the entrance of* VALENTINE.) Susan, I hate him. Oh, Susan, I could hate him if it were not for his poor hand.

MISS SUSAN. My dear.

PHOEBE. He thought I was old, because I am weary, and he should not have forgotten. I am only thirty. Susan, why does thirty seem so much more than twenty-nine? (*As if* VALENTINE *were present.*) Oh, sir, how dare you look so pityingly at me? Because I have had to work so hard,—is it a crime when a woman works? Because I have tried to be courageous—have I been courageous, Susan?

MISS SUSAN. God knows you have.

PHOEBE. But it has given me the headache, it has tired my eyes. Alas, Miss Phoebe, all your charm has gone, for you have the headache, and your eyes are tired. He is dancing with Charlotte Parratt now, Susan. 'I vow, Miss Charlotte, you are selfish and silly, but you are sweet eighteen.' 'Oh la, Captain Brown, what a quiz you are.' That delights him, Susan; see how he waggles his silly head.

MISS SUSAN.   Charlotte Parratt is a goose.

PHOEBE.   'Tis what gentlemen prefer. If there were a sufficient number of geese to go round, Susan, no woman of sense would ever get a husband. 'Charming Miss Charlotte, you are like a garden; Miss Phoebe was like a garden once, but 'tis a faded garden now.'

MISS SUSAN.   If to be ladylike——

PHOEBE.   Susan, I am tired of being ladylike. I am a young woman still, and to be ladylike is not enough. I wish to be bright and thoughtless and merry. It is every woman's birthright to be petted and admired; I wish to be petted and admired. Was I born to be confined within these four walls? Are they the world, Susan, or is there anything beyond them? I want to know. My eyes are tired because for ten years they have seen nothing but maps

and desks.   Ten years!   Ten years ago I went
to bed a young girl and I woke with this cap on
my head.   It is not fair.   This is not me, Susan,
this is some other person, I want to be myself.

MISS SUSAN.   Phoebe, Phoebe, you who have
always been so patient!

PHOEBE.   Oh no, not always.   If you only
knew how I have rebelled at times, you would
turn from me in horror.   Susan, I have a
picture of myself as I used to be; I sometimes
look at it.   I sometimes kiss it, and say, 'Poor
girl, they have all forgotten you.   But I remember.'

MISS SUSAN.   I cannot recall it.

PHOEBE.   I keep it locked away in my room.
Would you like to see it?   I shall bring it down.
My room!   Oh, Susan, it is there that the
Phoebe you think so patient has the hardest fight
with herself, for there I have seemed to hear and
see the Phoebe of whom this (*looking at herself*)
is but an image in a distorted glass.   I have
heard her singing as if she thought she was still
a girl.   I have heard her weeping; perhaps it
was only I who was weeping; but she seemed

to cry to me, 'Let me out of this prison, give me back the years you have taken from me. Oh, where are my pretty curls?' she cried. 'Where is my youth, my youth.'

(*She goes out, leaving* MISS SUSAN *woeful. Presently* SUSAN *takes up the algebra book and reads.*)

MISS SUSAN. 'A stroke B multiplied by B stroke C equal AB stroke a little 2; stroke AC add BC. "Poor Phoebe!" Multiply by C stroke A and we get—Poor Phoebe! C a B stroke a little 2 stroke AC little 2 add BC. "Oh, I cannot believe it!" Stroke a little 2 again, add AB little 2 add a little 2 C stroke a BC.' . . .

(PATTY *comes in with the lamp.*)

PATTY. Hurting your poor eyes reading without a lamp. Think shame, Miss Susan.

MISS SUSAN (*with spirit*). Patty, I will not be dictated to. (PATTY *looks out at window.*) Draw the curtains at once. I cannot allow you to stand gazing at the foolish creatures who crowd to a ball.

PATTY (*closing curtains*). I am not gazing at them, ma'am; I am gazing at my sweetheart.

MISS SUSAN. Your sweetheart? (*Softly.*) I did not know you had one.

PATTY. Nor have I, ma'am, as yet. But I looks out, and thinks I to myself, at any moment he may turn the corner. I ha' been looking out at windows waiting for him to oblige by turning the corner this fifteen years.

MISS SUSAN. Fifteen years, and still you are hopeful?

PATTY. There is not a more hopeful woman in all the king's dominions.

MISS SUSAN. You who are so much older than Miss Phoebe.

PATTY. Yes, ma'am, I ha' the advantage of her by ten years.

MISS SUSAN. It would be idle to pretend that you are specially comely.

PATTY. That may be, but my face is my own, and the more I see it in the glass the more it pleases me. I never look at it but I say to myself, 'Who is to be the lucky man?'

MISS SUSAN. 'Tis wonderful.

PATTY. This will be a great year for females, ma'am. Think how many of the men that marched away strutting to the wars have come back limping. Who is to take off their wooden legs of an evening, Miss Susan? You, ma'am, or me?

MISS SUSAN. Patty!

PATTY (*doggedly*). Or Miss Phoebe? (*With feeling.*) The pretty thing that she was, Miss Susan.

MISS SUSAN. Do you remember, Patty? I think there is no other person who remembers unless it be the Misses Willoughby and Miss Henrietta.

PATTY (*eagerly*). Give her a chance, ma'am, and take her to the balls. There be three of them this week, and the last ball will be the best, for 'tis to be at the barracks, and you will need a carriage to take you there, and there will be the packing of you into it by gallant squires and the unpacking of you out, and other devilries.

MISS SUSAN. Patty!

PATTY. If Miss Phoebe were to dress young again and put candles in her eyes that used to be so bright, and coax back her curls——

(PHOEBE *returns, and a great change*

*has come over her. She is young and
pretty again. She is wearing the wedding-
gown of* ACT I., *her ringlets are glorious,
her figure youthful, her face flushed and
animated.* PATTY *is the first to see her,
and is astonished.* PHOEBE *signs to her
to go.*)

PHOEBE (*when* PATTY *has gone*). Susan. (MISS
SUSAN *sees and is speechless.*) Susan, this is the
picture of my old self that I keep locked away
in my room, and sometimes take out of its
box to look at. This is the girl who kisses
herself in the glass and sings and dances with
glee until I put her away frightened lest you
should hear her.

MISS SUSAN. How marvellous! Oh, Phoebe.

PHOEBE. Perhaps I should not do it, but it
is so easy. I have but to put on the old wedding-
gown and tumble my curls out of the cap.
(*Passionately.*) Sister, am I as changed as he
says I am?

MISS SUSAN. You almost frighten me.

(*The band is heard.*)

PHOEBE. The music is calling to us. Susan,

I will celebrate Waterloo in a little ball of my own. See, my curls have begun to dance, they are so anxious to dance. One dance, Susan, to Phoebe of the ringlets, and then I will put her away in her box and never look at her again. Ma'am, may I have the honour? Nay, then I shall dance alone. (*She dances.*) Oh, Susan, I almost wish I were a goose.

> (*Presently* PATTY *returns. She gazes at* MISS PHOEBE *dancing.*)

PATTY. Miss Phoebe!

PHOEBE (*still dancing*). Not Miss Phoebe, Patty. I am not myself to-night, I am—let me see, I am my niece.

PATTY (*in a whisper to* SUSAN). But Miss Susan, 'tis Captain Brown.

MISS SUSAN. Oh, stop, Phoebe, stop!

PATTY. Nay, let him see her!

> (MISS SUSAN *hurries scandalised into the other room as* VALENTINE *enters.*)

VALENTINE. I ventured to come back be-cause—— (PHOEBE) *turns to him—he stops abruptly, bewildered.*) I beg your pardon, madam, I thought it was Miss Susan or Miss Phoebe.

> (*His mistake surprises her, but she is in a wild mood and curtsies, then turns away and smiles. He stares as if half-convinced.*)

PATTY (*with an inspiration*). 'Tis my mistresses' niece, sir; she is on a visit here.

> (*He is deceived. He bows gallantly, then remembers the object of his visit. He produces a bottle of medicine.*)

VALENTINE. Patty, I obtained this at the apothecary's for Miss Phoebe's headache. It should be taken at once.

PATTY. Miss Phoebe is lying down, sir.

VALENTINE. Is she asleep?

PATTY (*demurely*). No, sir, I think she be wide awake.

VALENTINE. It may soothe her.

PHOEBE. Patty, take it to Aunt Phoebe at once.

> (PATTY *goes out sedately with the medicine.*)

VALENTINE (*after a little awkwardness, which*

PHOEBE *enjoys*). Perhaps I may venture to present myself, Miss—Miss——?

PHOEBE. Miss—Livvy, sir.

VALENTINE. I am Captain Brown, Miss Livvy, an old friend of both your aunts.

PHOEBE (*curtsying*). I have heard them speak of a dashing Mr. Brown. But I think it cannot be the same.

VALENTINE (*a little chagrined*). Why not, ma'am?

PHOEBE. I ask your pardon, sir.

VALENTINE. I was sure you must be related. Indeed, for a moment the likeness—even the voice——

PHOEBE (*pouting*). La, sir, you mean I am like Aunt Phoebe. Every one says so—and indeed 'tis no compliment.

VALENTINE. 'Twould have been a compliment once. You must be a daughter of the excellent Mr. James Throssel who used to reside at Great Buckland.

PHOEBE. He is still there.

VALENTINE. A tedious twenty miles from here, as I remember.

PHOEBE.   La! I have found the journey a
monstrous quick one, sir.

>   (*The band is again heard.   She runs to the
>   window to peep between the curtains, and
>   his eyes follow her admiringly.*)

VALENTINE (*eagerly*).   Miss Livvy, you go to
the ball?

PHOEBE.   Alas, sir, I have no card.

VALENTINE.   I have two cards for your
aunts.   As Miss Phoebe has the headache, your
Aunt Susan must take you to the ball.

PHOEBE.   Oh, oh! (*Her feet move to the
music.*)   Sir, I cannot control my feet.

VALENTINE.   They are already at the ball,
ma'am; you must follow them.

PHOEBE (*with all the pent-up mischief of ten
years*).   Oh, sir, do you think some pretty
gentleman might be partial to me at the ball?

VALENTINE.   If that is your wish——

PHOEBE.   I should love, sir, to inspire frenzy
in the breast of the male. (*With sudden col-
lapse.*)   I dare not go—I dare not.

VALENTINE.   Miss Livvy, I vow——

>   (*He turns eagerly to* MISS SUSAN, *who enters.*)

I have ventured, Miss Susan, to introduce myself to your charming niece.

> (MISS SUSAN *would like to run away
> again, but the wicked* MISS PHOEBE *is
> determined to have her help.*)

PHOEBE. Aunt Susan, do not be angry with your Livvy—your Livvy, Aunt Susan. This gentleman says he is the dashing Mr. Brown, he has cards for us for the ball, Auntie. Of course we cannot go—we dare not go. Oh, Auntie, hasten into your bombazine.

MISS SUSAN (*staggered*). Phoebe——

PHOEBE. Aunt Phoebe wants me to go. If I say she does you know she does !

MISS SUSAN. But my dear, my dear.

PHOEBE. Oh, Auntie, why do you talk so much. Come, come.

VALENTINE. I shall see to it, Miss Susan, that your niece has a charming ball.

PHOEBE. He means he will find me sweet partners.

VALENTINE. Nay, ma'am, I mean *I* shall be your partner.

PHOEBE (*who is not an angel*). Aunt Susan, he still dances!

VALENTINE. *Still*, ma'am?

PHOEBE. Oh, sir, you are indeed dashing. Nay, sir, please not to scowl, I could not avoid noticing them.

VALENTINE. Noticing what, Miss Livvy?

PHOEBE. The grey hairs, sir.

VALENTINE. I vow, ma'am, there is not one in my head.

PHOEBE. He is such a quiz. I so love a quiz.

VALENTINE. Then, ma'am, I shall do nothing but quiz you at the ball. Miss Susan, I beg you——

MISS SUSAN. Oh, sir, dissuade her.

VALENTINE. Nay, I entreat.

PHOEBE. Auntie!

MISS SUSAN. Think, my dear, think, we dare not.

PHOEBE (*shuddering*). No, we dare not, I cannot go.

VALENTINE. Indeed, ma'am.

PHOEBE. 'Tis impossible.

(She really means it, and had not the music here taken an unfair advantage of her it is certain that MISS PHOEBE would never have gone to the ball. In after years she and MISS SUSAN would have talked together of the monstrous evening when she nearly lost her head, but regained it before it could fall off. But suddenly the music swells so alluringly that it is a thousand fingers beckoning her to all the balls she has missed, and in a transport she whirls MISS SUSAN from the blue and white room to the bed-chamber where is the bombazine. VALENTINE awaits their return like a conqueror, until MISS LIVVY'S words about his hair return to trouble him. He is stooping, gazing intently into a small mirror, extracting the grey hairs one by one, when PATTY ushers in the sisters WILLOUGHBY and MISS HENRIETTA. MISS HENRIETTA is wearing the new veil, which opens or closes like curtains when she pulls a string. She opens it now to see what he is doing, and the slight sound brings him to his feet.)

MISS HENRIETTA.   'Tis but the new veil, sir; there is no cause for alarm.

(*They have already learned from* PATTY, *we may be sure, that he is in the house, but they express genteel surprise.*)

MISS FANNY.   Mary, surely we are addressing the gallant Captain Brown!

VALENTINE.   It is the Misses Willoughby and Miss Henrietta.   'Tis indeed a gratification to renew acquaintance with such elegant and respectable females.

(*The greetings are elaborate.*)

MISS WILLOUGHBY.   You have seen Miss Phoebe, sir?

VALENTINE.   I have had the honour.   Miss Phoebe, I regret to say, is now lying down with the headache.   (*The ladies are too delicately minded to exchange glances before a man, but they are privately of opinion that this meeting after ten years with the dazzling* BROWN *has laid* MISS PHOEBE *low.   They are in a twitter of sympathy with her, and yearning to see* MISS SUSAN *alone, so that they may draw from her an account of the exciting meeting.*) You do not favour the ball to-night?

MISS FANNY.   I confess balls are distasteful to me.

MISS HENRIETTA.   'Twill be a mixed assembly. I am credibly informed that the woollen draper's daughter has obtained a card.

VALENTINE (*gravely*).   Good God, ma'am, is it possible?

MISS WILLOUGHBY.   We shall probably spend the evening here with Miss Susan at the card table.

VALENTINE.   But Miss Susan goes with me to the ball, ma'am.

> (*This is scarcely less exciting to them than the overthrow of the Corsican.*)

VALENTINE.   Nay, I hope there be no impropriety.   Miss Livvy will accompany her.

MISS WILLOUGHBY (*bewildered*).   Miss Livvy?

VALENTINE.   Their charming niece.

> (*The ladies repeat the word in a daze.*)

MISS FANNY.   They had not apprised us that they have a visitor.

> (*They think this reticence unfriendly, and are wondering whether they ought not to retire hurt, when* MISS SUSAN *enters in her*

*bombazine, wraps, and bonnet. She starts
at sight of them, and has the bearing of a
guilty person.)*

MISS WILLOUGHBY (*stiffly*). We have but now
been advertised of your intention for this evening, Susan.

MISS HENRIETTA. We deeply regret **our**
intrusion.

MISS SUSAN (*wistfully*). Please not to be
piqued, Mary. 'Twas so—sudden.

MISS WILLOUGHBY. I cannot remember,
Susan, that your estimable brother had a
daughter. I thought all the three were
sons.

MISS SUSAN (*with deplorable readiness*). Three
sons and a daughter. Surely you remember
little Livvy, Mary?

MISS WILLOUGHBY (*bluntly*). No, Susan, I
do not.

MISS SUSAN. I—I must go. I hear Livvy
calling.

MISS FANNY (*tartly*). I hear nothing but the
band. We are not to see your niece?

MISS SUSAN. Another time—to-morrow.

Pray rest a little before you depart, Mary.   I—
I—Phoebe Livvy—the headache——

> (*But before she can go another lady enters
> gaily.*)

VALENTINE.   Ah, here is Miss Livvy.

> (*The true culprit is more cunning than*
> MISS SUSAN, *and before they can see her
> she quickly pulls the strings of her bonnet,
> which is like* MISS HENRIETTA'S, *and it
> obscures her face.*)

MISS SUSAN.   This—this is my niece, Livvy—
Miss Willoughby, Miss Henrietta, Miss Fanny
Willoughby.

VALENTINE.   Ladies, excuse my impatience,
but——

MISS WILLOUGHBY.   One moment, sir.   May
I ask, Miss Livvy, how many brothers you
have.

PHOEBE.   Two.

MISS WILLOUGHBY.   I thank you.

> (*She looks strangely at* MISS SUSAN, *and*
> MISS PHOEBE *knows that she has blundered.*)

PHOEBE (*at a venture*).   Excluding the unhappy Thomas.

MISS SUSAN (*clever for the only moment in her life*).   We never mention him.

> (*They are swept away on the arms of the impatient* CAPTAIN.)

MISS WILLOUGHBY, MISS HENRIETTA, AND MISS FANNY.   What has Thomas done?

> (*They have no suspicion as yet of what* MISS PHOEBE *has done; but they believe there is a scandal in the Throssel family, and they will not sleep happily until they know what it is.*)

End of Act II.

ACT III

ACT III

THE BALL

A ball, but not the one to which we have seen Miss Susan and Miss Phoebe rush forth upon their career of crime. This is the third of the series, the one of which Patty has foretold with horrid relish that it promises to be specially given over to devilries. The scene is a canvas pavilion, used as a retiring room and for card play, and through an opening in the back we have glimpses of gay uniforms and fair ladies intermingled in the bravery of the dance. There is coming and going through this opening, and also through slits in the canvas. The pavilion is fantastically decorated in various tastes, and is lit with lanterns. A good-natured moon, nevertheless, shines into it benignly. Some of the card tables are neglected, but at one a game of quadrille is in progress. There is much movement and hilarity, but none from one side of the tent, where sit several young ladies, all pretty, all appealing and all woeful, for no gallant comes to ask them if he may have the felicity. The nervous woman chaperoning them, and afraid to meet their gaze lest they scowl or weep in reply, is no other than Miss Susan, the most unhappy Miss Susan we have yet seen; she sits there gripping her composure in both hands. Far less susceptible to shame is the brazen Phoebe, who may be seen passing the opening on the arm of a cavalier, and flinging her trembling sister a mischievous kiss. The younger ladies note the incident; alas, they are probably meant to notice it, and they cower, as under a blow.

HARRIET (*a sad-eyed, large girl, who we hope found a romance at her next ball*). Are we so disagreeable that no one will dance with us? Miss Susan, 'tis infamous; they have eyes for no one but your niece.

CHARLOTTE. Miss Livvy has taken Ensign Blades from me.

HARRIET. If Miss Phoebe were here, I am sure she would not allow her old pupils to be so neglected.

(*The only possible reply for* MISS SUSAN *is to make herself look as small as possible. A lieutenant comes to them, once a scorner*

of woman, but now SPICER *the bewitched.*
HARRIET *has a moment's hope.*)

How do you do, sir?

SPICER (*with dreadful indifference, though she is his dear cousin*). Nay, ma'am, how do *you* do? (*Wistfully.*) May I stand beside you, Miss Susan?

> (*He is a most melancholic young man, and he fidgets her.*)

MISS SUSAN (*with spirit*). You have been standing beside me, sir, nearly all the evening.

SPICER (*humbly. It is strange to think that he had been favourably mentioned in despatches*). Indeed, I cannot but be cognisant of the sufferings I cause by attaching myself to you in this unseemly manner. Accept my assurances, ma'am, that you have my deepest sympathy.

MISS SUSAN. Then why do you do it?

SPICER. Because you are her aunt, ma'am. It is a scheme of mine by which I am in hopes to soften her heart. Her affection for you, ma'am, is beautiful to observe, and if she could be persuaded that I seek her hand from a passionate desire to have you for my Aunt Susan—do you perceive anything hopeful in my scheme, ma'am?

MISS SUSAN. No, sir, I do not.

(SPICER *wanders away gloomily, takes too much to drink, and ultimately becomes a general.* ENSIGN BLADES *appears, frowning, and* CHARLOTTE *ventures to touch his sleeve.*)

CHARLOTTE. Ensign Blades, I have not danced with you once this evening.

BLADES (*with the cold brutality of a lover to another she*). Nor I with you, Charlotte. (*To* SUSAN.) May I solicit of you, Miss Susan, is Captain Brown Miss Livvy's guardian; is he affianced to her?

MISS SUSAN. No, sir.

BLADES. Then by what right, ma'am, does he interfere? Your elegant niece had consented to accompany me to the shrubbery—to look at the moon. And now Captain Brown forbids it. 'Tis unendurable.

CHARLOTTE. But you may see the moon from here, sir.

BLADES (*glancing at it contemptuously*). I

believe not, ma'am. (*The moon still shines on.*)

MISS SUSAN (*primly*).   I am happy Captain Brown forbade her.

BLADES.   Miss Susan, 'twas but because he is to conduct her to the shrubbery himself.

> (*He flings out pettishly, and* MISS SUSAN *looks pityingly at the wall-flowers.*)

MISS SUSAN.   My poor Charlotte!   May I take you to some very agreeable ladies?

CHARLOTTE (*tartly*).   No, you may not.   I am going to the shrubbery to watch Miss Livvy.

MISS SUSAN.   Please not to do that.

CHARLOTTE (*implying that* MISS SUSAN *will be responsible for her early death*).   My chest is weak.   I shall sit among the dew.

MISS SUSAN.   Charlotte, you terrify me.   At least, please to put this cloak about your shoulders.   Nay, my dear, allow me.

> (*She puts a cloak around* CHARLOTTE, *who departs vindictively for the shrubbery. She will not find* LIVVY *there, however, for next moment* MISS PHOEBE *darts in from the back.*)

PHOEBE (*in a gay whisper*). Susan, another offer—Major Linkwater—rotund man, black whiskers, fierce expression; he has rushed away to destroy himself.

(*We have been unable to find any record of the Major's tragic end.*)

AN OLD SOLDIER (*looking up from a card table, whence he has heard the raging of* BLADES). Miss Livvy, ma'am, what is this about the moon?

(PHOEBE *smiles roguishly.*)

PHOEBE (*looking about her*). I want my cloak, Aunt Susan.

MISS SUSAN. I have just lent it to poor Charlotte Parratt.

PHOEBE. Oh, auntie!

OLD SOLDIER. And now Miss Livvy cannot go into the shrubbery to see the moon; and she is so fond of the moon!

(MISS PHOEBE *screws her nose at him merrily, and darts back to the dance, but she has left a defender behind her.*)

A GALLANT (*whose name we have not succeeded in discovering*). Am I to understand, sir, that you are intimating disparagement of the moon? If a certain female has been graciously pleased to signify approval of that orb, any slight cast upon the moon, sir, I shall regard as a personal affront.

OLD SOLDIER.   Hoity-toity.

(*But he rises, and they face each other, as* MISS SUSAN *feels, for battle. She is about to rush between their undrawn swords when there is a commotion outside; a crowd gathers and opens to allow some officers to assist a fainting woman into the tent. It is* MISS PHOEBE, *and* MISS SUSAN *with a cry goes on her knees beside her. The tent has filled with the sympathetic and inquisitive, but* CAPTAIN BROWN, *as a physician, takes command, and by his order they retire. He finds difficulty in bringing the sufferer to, and gets little help from* MISS SUSAN, *who can only call upon* MISS PHOEBE *by name.*)

VALENTINE.   Nay, Miss Susan, 'tis useless calling for Miss Phoebe. 'Tis my fault; I should not have permitted Miss Livvy to dance so immoderately. Why do they delay with the cordial?

> (*He goes to the back to close the open-ing, and while he is doing so the incom-prehensible* MISS PHOEBE *seizes the oppor-tunity to sit up on her couch of chairs, waggle her finger at* MISS SUSAN, *and sign darkly that she is about to make a genteel recovery.*)

PHOEBE. Where am I? Is that you, Aunt Susan? What has happened?

VALENTINE (*returning*). Nay, you must recline, Miss Livvy. You fainted. You have over-fatigued yourself.

PHOEBE. I remember.

> (BLADES *enters with the cordial.*)

VALENTINE. You will sip this cordial.

BLADES. By your leave, sir.

> (*He hands it to* PHOEBE *himself.*)

VALENTINE. She is in restored looks already, Miss Susan.

PHOEBE. I am quite recovered. Perhaps if you were to leave me now with my excellent aunt——

VALENTINE. Be off with you, apple cheeks.

BLADES. Sir, I will suffer no reference to my complexion; and, if I mistake not, this charming lady was addressing you.

PHOEBE. If you please, both of you. (*They retire together, and no sooner have they gone than* MISS PHOEBE *leaps from the couch, her eyes sparkling. She presses the cordial on* MISS SUSAN.) Nay, drink it, Susan. I left it for you on purpose. I have such awful information to impart. Drink. (MISS SUSAN *drinks tremblingly and then the bolt is fired.*) Susan, Miss Henrietta and Miss Fanny are here!

MISS SUSAN. Phoebe!

PHOEBE. Suddenly my eyes lighted on them. At once I slipped to the ground.

MISS SUSAN. You think they did not see you?

PHOEBE. I am sure of it. They talked for a moment to Ensign Blades, and then turned and seemed to be going towards the shrubbery.

MISS SUSAN. He had heard that you were there with Captain Brown. He must have told them.

PHOEBE. I was not. But oh, sister, I am sure they suspect, else why should they be here? They never frequent balls.

MISS SUSAN. They have suspected for a week, ever since they saw you in your veil, Phoebe, on the night of the first dance. How could they but suspect, when they have visited us every day since then and we have always pretended that Livvy was gone out.

PHOEBE. Should they see my face it will be idle to attempt to deceive them.

MISS SUSAN. Idle indeed; Phoebe, the scandal! You—a schoolmistress!

PHOEBE. That is it, sister. A little happiness has gone to my head like strong waters.

(*She is very restless and troubled.*)

MISS SUSAN. My dear, stand still, and think.

PHOEBE. I dare not, I cannot. Oh, Susan, if they see me we need not open school again.

MISS SUSAN. We shall starve.

PHOEBE (*passionately*). This horrid, forward, flirting, heartless, hateful little toad of a Livvy.

MISS SUSAN. Brother James's daughter, as we call her!

PHOEBE. 'Tis all James's fault.

MISS SUSAN. Sister, when you know that James has no daughter!

PHOEBE. If he had really had one, think you I could have been so wicked as to personate her? Susan, I know not what I am saying, but you know who it is that has turned me into this wild creature.

MISS SUSAN. Oh, Valentine Brown, how could you?

PHOEBE. To weary of Phoebe—patient, lady-like Phoebe—the Phoebe whom I have lost—to turn from her with a 'Bah, you make me old,' and become enamoured in a night of a thing like this!

MISS SUSAN. Yes, yes, indeed; yet he has been kind to us also. He has been to visit us several times.

PHOEBE. In the hope to see her. Was he not most silent and gloomy when we said she was gone out?

MISS SUSAN. He is infatuate—— (*She hesitates.*) Sister, you are not partial to him still?

PHOEBE. No, Susan, no. I did love him all those years, though I never spoke of it to you. I put hope aside at once, I folded it up and kissed it and put it away like a pretty garment I could never wear again, I but loved to think of him as a noble man. But he is not a noble man, and Livvy found it out in an hour. The gallant! I flirted that I might enjoy his fury. Susan, there has been a declaration in his eyes all to-night, and when he cries 'Adorable Miss Livvy, be mine,' I mean to answer with an 'Oh, la, how ridiculous you are. You are much too old—I have been but quizzing you, sir.'

MISS SUSAN. Phoebe, how can you be so cruel?

PHOEBE. Because he has taken from me the one great glory that is in a woman's life. Not a man's love—she can do without that—but her own dear sweet love for him. He is un-worthy of my love; that is why I can be so cruel.

MISS SUSAN. Oh, dear.

PHOEBE. And now my triumph is to be

denied me, for we must steal away home before Henrietta and Fanny see us.

MISS SUSAN.   Yes, yes.

PHOEBE (*dispirited*). And to-morrow we must say that Livvy has gone back to her father, for I dare keep up this deception no longer.   Susan, let us go.

> (*They are going dejectedly, but are arrested by the apparition of* MISS HENRIETTA *and* MISS FANNY *peeping into the tent.* PHOEBE *has just time to signify to her sister that she will confess all and beg for mercy, when the intruders speak.*)

MISS HENRIETTA (*not triumphant but astounded*). You, Miss Phoebe?

PHOEBE (*with bowed head*).   Yes.

MISS FANNY. How amazing! You do not deny, ma'am, that you are Miss Phoebe?

PHOEBE (*making confession*).   Yes, Fanny, I am Miss Phoebe.

> (*To her bewilderment* HENRIETTA *and* FANNY *exchange ashamed glances.*)

MISS HENRIETTA.   Miss Phoebe, we have done you a cruel wrong.

MISS FANNY. Phoebe, we apologise.

MISS HENRIETTA. To think how excitedly we have been following her about in the shrubbery.

MISS FANNY. She is wearing your cloak.

MISS HENRIETTA. Ensign Blades told us she was gone to the shrubbery.

MISS FANNY. And we were convinced there was no such person.

MISS HENRIETTA. So of course we thought it must be you.

MISS FANNY (*who has looked out*). I can discern her in the shrubbery still. She is decidedly taller than Phoebe.

MISS HENRIETTA. I thought she looked taller. I meant to say so. Phoebe, 'twas the cloak deceived us. We could not see her face.

PHOEBE (*beginning to understand*). Cloak? You mean, Henrietta—you mean, Fanny——

MISS FANNY. 'Twas wicked of us, my dear, but we—we thought that you and Miss Livvy were the same person. (*They have evidently been stalking* CHARLOTTE *in* MISS PHOEBE'S *cloak.* MISS SUSAN *shudders, but* MISS PHOEBE *utters a*

cry of reproach, and it is some time before they can
persuade her to forgive them.   It is of course also
some time before we can forgive MISS PHOEBE.)
Phoebe, you look so pretty.   Are they paying
you no attentions, my dear?

> (PHOEBE *is unable to resist these delight-*
> *ful openings.   The imploring looks* MISS
> SUSAN *gives her but add to her enjoyment.*
> *It is as if the sense of fun she had caged a*
> *moment ago were broke loose again.*)

PHOEBE.   Alas, they think of none but Livvy.
They come to me merely to say that they adore
her.

MISS HENRIETTA.   Surely not Captain Brown?

PHOEBE.   He is infatuate about her.

MISS FANNY.   Poor Phoebe!

> (*They make much of her, and she purrs*
> *naughtily to their stroking, with lightning*
> *peeps at* MISS SUSAN. *Affronted Pro-*
> *vidence seeks to pay her out by sending*
> ENSIGN BLADES *into the tent.   Then the*
> *close observer may see* MISS PHOEBE'S
> *heart sink like a bucket in a well.* MISS
> SUSAN *steals from the tent.*)

MISS HENRIETTA. Mr. Blades, I have been saying that if I were a gentleman I would pay my addresses to Miss Phoebe much rather than to her niece.

BLADES. Ma'am, excuse me.

MISS HENRIETTA (*indignant that* MISS PHOEBE *should be slighted so publicly*). Sir, you are a most ungallant and deficient young man.

BLADES. Really, ma'am, I assure you——

MISS HENRIETTA. Not another word, sir.

PHOEBE (*in her most old-maidish manner*). Miss Fanny, Miss Henrietta, it is time I spoke plainly to this gentleman. Please leave him to me. Surely 'twill come best from me.

MISS HENRIETTA. Indeed, yes, if it be not too painful to you.

PHOEBE. I must do my duty.

MISS FANNY (*wistfully*). If we could remain—

PHOEBE. Would it be seemly, Miss Fanny?

MISS HENRIETTA. Come, Fanny. (*To* BLADES.) Sir, you bring your punishment upon yourself.

> (*They press* PHOEBE'S *hand, and go. Her heart returns to its usual abode.*)

BLADES (*bewildered*).   Are you angry with me, Miss Livvy?

PHOEBE.   Oh, no.

BLADES.   Miss Livvy, I have something to say to you of supreme importance to me.   With regard to my complexion, I am aware, Miss Livvy, that it has retained a too youthful bloom. My brother officers comment on it with a certain lack of generosity.   (*Anxiously.*)   Might I inquire, ma'am, whether you regard my complexion as a subject for light talk.

PHOEBE.   No indeed, sir, I only wish I had it.

BLADES (*who has had no intention of offering, but is suddenly carried off his feet by the excellence of the opportunity, which is no doubt responsible for many proposals*).   Miss Livvy, ma'am, you may have it.

> (*She has a great and humorous longing that she could turn before his affrighted eyes into the schoolmistress she really is. She would endure much to be able at this moment to say, 'I have listened to you,* ENSIGN BLADES, *with attention, but I am really* MISS PHOEBE, *and I must now re-*

quest you to fetch me the implement.'
Under the shock, would he have sur-
rendered his palm for punishment? It
can never be known, for as she looks at
him longingly, LIEUTENANT SPICER *enters,*
and he mistakes the meaning of that longing
look.)

SPICER. 'Tis my dance, ma'am—'tis not
Ensign Blades'.

BLADES. Leave us, sir. We have matter of
moment to discuss.

SPICER (*fearing the worst*). His affection, Miss
Livvy, is not so deep as mine. He is a light and
shallow nature.

PHOEBE. Pooh! You are both light and
shallow natures.

BLADES. Both, ma'am? (*But he is not sure
that he has not had a miraculous escape.*)

PHOEBE (*severely*). 'Tis such as you, with your
foolish flirting ways, that confuse the minds of
women and make us try to be as silly as your-
selves.

SPICER (*crushed*). Ma'am.

PHOEBE. I did not mean to hurt you. (*She*

takes a hand of each and tries to advise them as if her curls were once more hidden under a cap.) You are so like little boys in a school. Do be good. Sit here beside me. I know you are very brave——

BLADES. Ha!

PHOEBE. And when you come back from the wars it must be so delightful to you to flirt with the ladies again.

SPICER. Oh, ma'am.

PHOEBE. As soon as you see a lady with a pretty nose you cannot help saying that you adore her.

BLADES (*in an ecstasy*). Nay, I swear.

PHOEBE. And you offer to her, not from love, but because you are so deficient in conversation.

SPICER. Charming, Miss Livvy.

PHOEBE (*with sudden irritation*). Oh, sir, go away; go away, both of you, and read improving books.

> (*They are cast down. She has not been quite fair to these gallants, for it is not really of them she has grown weary so much*

as of the lady they temporarily adore. If
MISS PHOEBE were to analyse her feelings
she would find that her remark is addressed
to LIVVY, and that it means, 'I have en-
joyed for a little pretending to be you, but I
am not you and I do not wish to be you.
Your glitter and the airs of you and
the racket of you tire me, I want to be done
with you, and to be back in quiet Quality
Street, of which I am a part; it is really
pleasant to me to know that I shall wake up
to-morrow slightly middle-aged.' With the
entrance of CAPTAIN BROWN, however, she
is at once a frivol again. He frowns at
sight of her cavaliers.)

VALENTINE. Gentlemen, I instructed this
lady to rest, and I am surprised to find you in
attendance. Miss Livvy, you must be weary
of their fatuities, and I have taken the liberty to
order your chaise.

PHOEBE. It is indeed a liberty.

BLADES. An outrage.

PHOEBE. I prefer to remain.

VALENTINE. Nay.

PHOEBE.   I promised this dance to Ensign Blades.

SPICER.   To me, ma'am.

PHOEBE.   And the following one to Lieutenant Spicer.   Mr. Blades, your arm.

VALENTINE.   I forbid any further dancing.

PHOEBE.   Forbid. La !

BLADES.   Sir, by what right——

VALENTINE.   By a right which I hope to make clear to Miss Livvy as soon as you gentlemen have retired.

> (PHOEBE *sees that the declaration is coming.*
> *She steels herself.*)

PHOEBE.   I am curious to know what Captain Brown can have to say to me.   In a few minutes, Mr. Blades, Lieutenant Spicer, I shall be at your service.

VALENTINE.   I trust not.

PHOEBE.   I give them my word.

> (*The young gentlemen retire, treading air*
> *once more.* BROWN *surveys her rather*
> *grimly.*)

VALENTINE.   You are an amazing pretty girl, ma'am, but you are a shocking flirt.

PHOEBE. La !

VALENTINE. It has somewhat diverted me to watch them go down before you. But I know you have a kind heart, and that if there be a rapier in your one hand there is a handkerchief in the other ready to staunch their wounds.

PHOEBE. I have not observed that they bled much.

VALENTINE. The Blades and the like, no. But one may, perhaps.

PHOEBE (*obviously the reference is to himself*). Perhaps I may wish to see him bleed.

VALENTINE (*grown stern*). For shame, Miss Livvy. (*Anger rises in her, but she wishes him to proceed.*) I speak, ma'am, in the interests of the man to whom I hope to see you affianced.

> (*No, she does not wish him to proceed. She had esteemed him for so long, she cannot have him debase himself before her now.*)

PHOEBE. Shall we—I have changed my mind, I consent to go home. Please to say nothing.

VALENTINE. Nay——

PHOEBE. I beg you.

VALENTINE. No. We must have it out.

PHOEBE. Then if you must go on, do so. But remember I begged you to desist. Who is this happy man?

(*His next words are a great shock to her.*)

VALENTINE. As to who he is, ma'am, of course I have no notion. Nor, I am sure, have you, else you would be more guarded in your conduct. But some day, Miss Livvy, the right man will come. Not to be able to tell him all, would it not be hard? And how could you acquaint him with this poor sport? His face would change, ma'am, as you told him of it, and yours would be a false face until it was told. This is what I have been so desirous to say to you—by the right of a friend.

PHOEBE (*in a low voice but bravely*). I see.

VALENTINE (*afraid that he has hurt her*). It has been hard to say and I have done it bunglingly. Ah, but believe me, Miss Livvy, it is not the flaunting flower men love; it is the modest violet.

PHOEBE. The modest violet! *You* dare to say that.

VALENTINE.   Yes, indeed, and when you are acquaint with what love really is——

PHOEBE.   Love! What do you know of love?

VALENTINE (*a little complacently*).   Why, ma'am, I know all about it.   I am in love, Miss Livvy.

PHOEBE (*with a disdainful inclination of the head*).   I wish you happy.

VALENTINE.   With a lady who was once very like you, ma'am.

> (*At first* PHOEBE *does not understand, then a suspicion of his meaning comes to her.*)

PHOEBE.   Not—not—oh no.

VALENTINE.   I had not meant to speak of it, but why should not I?   It will be a fine lesson to you, Miss Livvy.   Ma'am, it is your Aunt Phoebe whom I love.

PHOEBE (*rigid*).   You do not mean that.

VALENTINE.   Most ardently.

PHOEBE.   It is not true; how dare you make sport of her.

VALENTINE.   Is it sport to wish she may be my wife?

PHOEBE. Your wife!

VALENTINE. If I could win her.

PHOEBE (*bewildered*). May I solicit, sir, for how long you have been attached to Miss Phoebe?

VALENTINE. For nine years, I think.

PHOEBE. You think!

VALENTINE. I want to be honest. Never in all that time had I thought myself in love. Your aunts were my dear friends, and while I was at the wars we sometimes wrote to each other, but they were only friendly letters. I presume the affection was too placid to be love.

PHOEBE. I think that would be Aunt Phoebe's opinion.

VALENTINE. Yet I remember, before we went into action for the first time—I suppose the fear of death was upon me—some of them were making their wills—I have no near relative—I left everything to these two ladies.

PHOEBE (*softly*). Did you?

(*What is it that* MISS PHOEBE *begins to see as she sits there so quietly, with her hands pressed together as if upon some treasure?*

It is PHOEBE *of the ringlets with the stain
taken out of her.*)

VALENTINE.   And when I returned a week
ago and saw Miss Phoebe, grown so tired-looking
and so poor——

PHOEBE.   The shock made you feel old, I
know.

VALENTINE.   No, Miss Livvy, but it filled me
with a sudden passionate regret that I had not
gone down in that first engagement.   They
would have been very comfortably left.

PHOEBE.   Oh, sir!

VALENTINE.   I am not calling it love.

PHOEBE.   It was sweet and kind, but it was
not love.

VALENTINE.   It is love now.

PHOEBE.   No, it is only pity.

VALENTINE.   It is love.

PHOEBE (*she smiles tremulously*).   You really
mean Phoebe—tired, unattractive Phoebe, that
woman whose girlhood is gone.   Nay, impossible.

VALENTINE (*stoutly*).   Phoebe of the fascinat-
ing playful ways, whose ringlets were once as

pretty as yours, ma'am. I have visited her in her home several times this week—you were always out—I thank you for that ! I was alone with her, and with fragrant memories of her.

PHOEBE. Memories ! Yes, that is the Phoebe you love, the bright girl of the past—not the schoolmistress in her old-maid's cap.

VALENTINE. There you wrong me, for I have discovered for myself that the schoolmistress in her old-maid's cap is the noblest Miss Phoebe of them all. (*If only he would go away, and let* MISS PHOEBE *cry*.) When I enlisted, I remember I compared her to a garden. I have often thought of that.

PHOEBE. 'Tis an old garden now.

VALENTINE. The paths, ma'am, are better shaded.

PHOEBE. The flowers have grown old-fashioned.

VALENTINE. They smell the sweeter. Miss Livvy, do you think there is any hope for me?

PHOEBE. There was a man whom Miss Phoebe loved—long ago. He did not love her.

VALENTINE. Now here was a fool !

PHOEBE.   He kissed her once.

VALENTINE.   If Miss Phoebe suffered him to do that she thought he loved her.

PHOEBE.   Yes, yes.   (*She has to ask him the ten years old question.*)   Do you opinion that this makes her action in allowing it less reprehensible?   It has been such a pain to her ever since.

VALENTINE.   How   like   Miss   Phoebe! (*Sternly.*)   But that man was a knave.

PHOEBE.   No, he was a good man—only a little—inconsiderate.   She knows now that he has even forgotten that he did it.   I suppose men are like that?

VALENTINE.   No, Miss Livvy, men are not like that.   I am a very average man, but I thank God I am not like that.

PHOEBE.   It was you.

VALENTINE (*after a pause*).   Did Miss Phoebe say that?

PHOEBE.   Yes.

VALENTINE.   Then it is true.

(*He is very grave and quiet.*)

PHOEBE.   It was raining and her face was

wet. You said you did it because her face was wet.

VALENTINE. I had quite forgotten.

PHOEBE. But she remembers, and how often do you think the shameful memory has made her face wet since? The face you love, Captain Brown, you were the first to give it pain. The tired eyes—how much less tired they might be if they had never known you. You who are torturing me with every word, what have you done to Miss Phoebe? You who think you can bring back the bloom to that faded garden, and all the pretty airs and graces that fluttered round it once like little birds before the nest is torn down—bring them back to her if you can, sir; it was you who took them away.

VALENTINE. I vow I shall do my best to bring them back. (MISS PHOEBE *shakes her head.*) Miss Livvy, with your help——

PHOEBE. My help! I have not helped. I tried to spoil it all.

VALENTINE (*smiling*). To spoil it? You mean that you sought to flirt even with me. Ah, I knew you did. But that is nothing.

PHOEBE. Oh, sir, if you could overlook
it.

VALENTINE. I do.

PHOEBE. And forget these hateful balls.

VALENTINE. Hateful! Nay, I shall never
call them that. They have done me too great a
service. It was at the balls that I fell in love
with Miss Phoebe.

PHOEBE. What can you mean?

VALENTINE. She who was never at a ball!
(*Checking himself humorously.*) But I must not
tell you, it might hurt you.

PHOEBE. Tell me.

VALENTINE (*gaily*). Then on your own head
be the blame. It is you who have made me love
her, Miss Livvy.

PHOEBE. Sir?

VALENTINE. Yes, it is odd, and yet very
simple. You who so resembled her as she was!
for an hour, ma'am, you bewitched me; yes, I
confess it, but 'twas only for an hour. How
like, I cried at first, but soon it was, how unlike.
There was almost nothing she would have said
that you said; you did so much that she would

have scorned to do.   But I must not say these things to you !

PHOEBE.   I ask it of you, Captain Brown.

VALENTINE.   Well! Miss Phoebe's 'lady-likeness,' on which she set such store that I used to make merry of the word—I gradually perceived that it is a woman's most beautiful garment, and the casket which contains all the adorable qualities that go to the making of a perfect female.   When Miss Livvy rolled her eyes—ah !

(*He stops apologetically.*)

PHOEBE.   Proceed, sir.

VALENTINE.   It but made me the more complacent that never in her life had Miss Phoebe been guilty of the slightest deviation from the strictest   propriety.   (*She shudders.*)   I was always conceiving her in your place.   Oh, it was monstrous unfair to you.   I stood looking at you, Miss Livvy, and seeing in my mind her and the pretty things she did, and you did not do; why, ma'am, that is how I fell in love with Miss Phoebe at the balls.

PHOEBE.   I thank you.

VALENTINE.   Ma'am, tell me, do you think there is any hope for me?

PHOEBE.   Hope!

VALENTINE.   I shall go to her. 'Miss Phoebe,' I will say—oh, ma'am, so reverently— 'Miss Phoebe, my beautiful, most estimable of women, let me take care of you for ever more.'

> (MISS PHOEBE *presses the words to her heart and then drops them.*)

PHOEBE.   Beautiful.   La, Aunt Phoebe!

VALENTINE.   Ah, ma'am, you may laugh at a rough soldier so much enamoured, but 'tis true. 'Marry me, Miss Phoebe,' I will say, 'and I will take you back through those years of hardships that have made your sweet eyes too patient. Instead of growing older you shall grow younger. We will travel back together to pick up the many little joys and pleasures you had to pass by when you trod that thorny path alone.'

PHOEBE.   Can't be—can't be.

VALENTINE.   Nay, Miss Phoebe has loved me. 'Tis you have said it.

PHOEBE.   I did not mean to tell you.

VALENTINE.   She will be my wife yet.

PHOEBE.   Never.

VALENTINE.   You are severe, Miss Livvy.
But it is because you are partial to her, and I
am happy of that.

PHOEBE (*in growing horror of herself*).   I
partial to her! I am laughing at both of you.
Miss Phoebe.   La, that old thing.

VALENTINE (*sternly*).   Silence!

PHOEBE.   I hate her and despise her.   If you
knew what she is——

(*He stops her with a gesture.*)

VALENTINE.   I know what you are.

PHOEBE.   That paragon who has never been
guilty of the slightest deviation from the strictest
propriety.

VALENTINE.   Never.

PHOEBE.   That garden——

VALENTINE.   Miss Livvy, for shame.

PHOEBE.   Your garden has been destroyed,
sir; the weeds have entered it, and all the
flowers are choked.

VALENTINE.   You false woman, what do you
mean?

PHOEBE.   I will tell you.   (*But his confidence awes her.*)   What faith you have in her.

VALENTINE.   As in my God.   Speak.

PHOEBE.   I cannot tell you.

VALENTINE.   No, you cannot.

PHOEBE.   It is too horrible.

VALENTINE.   You are too horrible.   Is not that it?

PHOEBE.   Yes, that is it.

(MISS SUSAN *has entered and caught the last words.*)

MISS SUSAN (*shrinking as from a coming blow*). What is too horrible?

VALENTINE.   Ma'am, I leave the telling of it to her, if she dare.   And I devoutly hope those are the last words I shall ever address to this lady.

(*He bows and goes out in dudgeon.* MISS SUSAN *believes all is discovered and that* MISS PHOEBE *is for ever shamed.*)

MISS SUSAN (*taking* PHOEBE *in her arms*).   My love, my dear, what terrible thing has he said to you?

PHOEBE (*forgetting everything but that she is*

loved).   Not terrible—glorious!   Susan, 'tis
Phoebe he loves, 'tis me, not Livvy!   He loves
me, he loves me!   Me—Phoebe!

> (MISS SUSAN'S *bosom swells.   It is her
> great hour as much as* PHOEBE'S.)

End of Act III.

ACT IV

ACT IV

THE BLUE AND WHITE ROOM

If we could shut our eyes to the two sisters sitting here in woe, this would be, to the male eye at least, the identical blue and white room of ten years ago ; the same sun shining into it and playing familiarly with Miss Susan's treasures. But the ladies are changed. It is not merely that Miss Phoebe has again donned her schoolmistress's gown and hidden her curls under the cap. To see her thus once more, her real self, after the escapade of the ball, is not unpleasant, and the cap and gown do not ill become the quiet room. But she now turns guiltily from the sun that used to be her intimate, her face is drawn, her form condensed into the smallest space, and her hands lie trembling in her lap. It is disquieting to note that any life there is in the room comes not from her but from Miss Susan. If the house were to go on fire now it would be she who would have to carry out Miss Phoebe.

Whatever of import has happened since the ball, Patty knows it, and is enjoying it. We see this as she

*ushers in Miss Willoughby. Note also, with concern,
that at mention of the visitor's name the eyes of the
sisters turn affrightedly, not to the door by which
their old friend enters, but to the closed door of the
spare bed-chamber. Patty also gives it a meaning
glance ; then the three look at each other, and two of
them blanch.*

MISS WILLOUGHBY (*the fourth to look at the
door*). I am just run across, Susan, to inquire
how Miss Livvy does now.

MISS SUSAN. She is still very poorly, Mary.

MISS WILLOUGHBY. I am so unhappy of that.
I conceive it to be a nervous disorder?

MISS SUSAN (*almost too glibly*). Accompanied
by trembling, flutterings, and spasms.

MISS WILLOUGHBY. The excitements of the
ball. You have summoned the apothecary at
last, I trust, Phoebe?

(MISS PHOEBE, *once so ready of defence,
can say nothing.*)

MISS SUSAN (*to the rescue*). It is Livvy's own
wish that he should not be consulted.

MISS WILLOUGHBY (*looking longingly at the door*). May I go in to see her?

MISS SUSAN. I fear not, Mary. She is almost asleep, and it is best not to disturb her. (*Peeping into the bedroom.*) Lie quite still, Livvy, my love, quite still.

> (*Somehow this makes* PATTY *smile so broadly that she finds it advisable to retire.*
> MISS WILLOUGHBY *sighs, and produces a small bowl from the folds of her cloak.*)

MISS WILLOUGHBY. This is a little arrowroot, of which I hope Miss Livvy will be so obliging as to partake.

MISS SUSAN (*taking the bowl*). I thank you, Mary.

PHOEBE (*ashamed*). Susan, we ought not——

MISS SUSAN (*shameless*). I will take it to her while it is still warm.

> (*She goes into the bedroom.* MISS WILLOUGHBY *gazes at* MISS PHOEBE, *who certainly shrinks. It has not escaped the notice of the visitor that* MISS PHOEBE *has become the more timid of the sisters, and she has evolved an explanation.*)

MISS WILLOUGHBY. Phoebe, has Captain Brown been apprised of Miss Livvy's illness?

PHOEBE (*uncomfortably*). I think not, Miss Willoughby.

MISS WILLOUGHBY (*sorry for* PHOEBE, *and speaking very kindly*). Is this right, Phoebe? You informed Fanny and Henrietta at the ball of his partiality for Livvy. My dear, it is hard for you, but have you any right to keep them apart?

PHOEBE (*discovering only now what are the suspicions of her friends*). Is that what you think I am doing, Miss Willoughby?

MISS WILLOUGHBY. Such a mysterious illness. (*Sweetly*) Long ago, Phoebe, I once caused much unhappiness through foolish jealousy. That is why I venture to hope that you will not be as I was, my dear.

PHOEBE. I jealous of Livvy!

MISS WILLOUGHBY (*with a sigh*). I thought as little of the lady I refer to, but he thought otherwise.

PHOEBE. Indeed, Miss Willoughby, you wrong me.

(*But* MISS WILLOUGHBY *does not entirely believe her, and there is a pause, so long a pause that unfortunately* MISS SUSAN *thinks she has left the house.*)

MISS SUSAN (*peeping in*). Is she gone?

MISS WILLOUGHBY (*hurt*). No, Susan, but I am going.

MISS SUSAN (*distressed*). Mary!

(*She follows her out, but* MISS WILLOUGHBY *will not be comforted, and there is a coldness between them for the rest of the day.* MISS SUSAN *is not so abashed as she ought to be. She returns, and partakes with avidity of the arrowroot.*)

MISS SUSAN. Phoebe, I am well aware that this is wrong of me, but Mary's arrowroot is so delicious. The ladies'-fingers and petticoat-tails those officers sent to Livvy, I ate them also! (*Once on a time this would have amused* MISS PHOEBE, *but her sense of humour has gone. She is crying.*) Phoebe, if you have such remorse you will weep yourself to death.

PHOEBE. Oh, sister, were it not for you, how gladly would I go into a decline.

MISS SUSAN (*after she has soothed* PHOEBE *a little*).   My dear, what is to be done about her? We cannot have her supposed to be here for ever.

PHOEBE.   We had to pretend that she was ill to keep her out of sight; and now we cannot say she has gone away, for the Miss Willoughby's windows command our door, and they are always watching.

MISS SUSAN (*peeping from the window*).   I see Fanny watching now. I feel, Phoebe, as if Livvy really existed.

PHOEBE (*mournfully*).   We shall never be able to esteem ourselves again.

MISS SUSAN (*who has in her the makings of a desperate criminal*).   Phoebe, why not marry him? If only we could make him think that Livvy had gone home. Then he need never know.

PHOEBE.   Susan, you pain me. She who marries without telling all—hers must ever be a false face.   They are his own words.

(PATTY *enters importantly*.)

PATTY.   Captain Brown.

PHOEBE (*starting up*). I wrote to him, begging him not to come.

MISS SUSAN (*quickly*). Patty, I am sorry we are out.

> (*But* VALENTINE *has entered in time to hear her words.*)

VALENTINE (*not unmindful that this is the room in which he is esteemed a wit*). I regret that they are out, Patty, but I will await their return. (*The astonishing man sits on the ottoman beside* MISS SUSAN, *but politely ignores her presence.*) It is not my wish to detain you, Patty.

> (PATTY *goes reluctantly, and the sisters think how like him, and how delightful it would be if they were still the patterns of propriety he considers them.*)

PHOEBE (*bravely*). Captain Brown.

VALENTINE (*rising*). You, Miss Phoebe. I hear Miss Livvy is indisposed?

PHOEBE. She is—very poorly.

VALENTINE. But it is not that unpleasant girl I have come to see, it is you.

MISS SUSAN (*meekly*). How do you do?

VALENTINE (*ignoring her*). And I am happy, Miss Phoebe, to find you alone.

MISS SUSAN (*appealingly*). How do you do, sir?

PHOEBE. You know quite well, sir, that Susan is here.

VALENTINE. Nay, ma'am, excuse me. I heard Miss Susan say she was gone out. Miss Susan is incapable of prevarication.

MISS SUSAN (*rising—helpless*). What am I to do?

PHOEBE. Don't go, Susan—'tis what he wants.

VALENTINE. I have her word that she is not present.

MISS SUSAN. Oh dear.

VALENTINE. My faith in Miss Susan is absolute. (*At this she retires into the bedroom, and immediately his manner changes. He takes* MISS PHOEBE'S *hands into his own kind ones.*) You coward, Miss Phoebe, to be afraid of Valentine Brown.

PHOEBE. I wrote and begged you not to come.

VALENTINE.   You implied as a lover, Miss Phoebe, but surely always as a friend.

PHOEBE.   Oh yes, yes.

VALENTINE.   You told Miss Livvy that you loved me once.   How carefully you hid it from me!

PHOEBE (*more firmly*).   A woman must never tell.   You went away to the great battles.   I was left to fight in a little one.   Women have a flag to fly, Mr. Brown, as well as men, and old maids have a flag as well as women.   I tried to keep mine flying.

VALENTINE.   But you ceased to care for me. (*Tenderly.*)   I dare ask your love no more, but I still ask you to put yourself into my keeping.   Miss Phoebe, let me take care of you.

PHOEBE.   It cannot be.

VALENTINE.   This weary teaching!   Let me close your school.

PHOEBE.   Please, sir.

VALENTINE.   If not for your own sake, I ask you, Miss Phoebe, to do it for mine.   In memory of the thoughtless recruit who went off laughing to the wars. They say ladies cannot quite forget the man who has used them ill; Miss Phoebe, do it for me because I used you ill.

PHOEBE. I beg you—no more.

VALENTINE (*manfully*). There, it is all ended. Miss Phoebe, here is my hand on it.

PHOEBE. What will you do now?

VALENTINE. I also must work. I will become a physician again, with some drab old housekeeper to neglect me and the house. Do you foresee the cobwebs gathering and gathering, Miss Phoebe?

PHOEBE. Oh, sir!

VALENTINE. You shall yet see me in Quality Street, wearing my stock all awry.

PHOEBE. Oh, oh!

VALENTINE. And with snuff upon my sleeve.

PHOEBE. Sir, sir!

VALENTINE. No skulker, ma'am, I hope, but gradually turning into a grumpy, crusty, bottle-nosed old bachelor.

PHOEBE. Oh, Mr. Brown!

VALENTINE. And all because you will not walk across the street with me.

PHOEBE. Indeed, sir, you must marry—and I hope it may be some one who is really like a garden.

VALENTINE. I know but one. That reminds me, Miss Phoebe, of something I had forgot. (*He produces a paper from his pocket.*) 'Tis a trifle I have wrote about you. But I fear to trouble you.

> (PHOEBE'S *hands go out longingly for it.*)

PHOEBE (*reading*). 'Lines to a Certain Lady, who is Modestly unaware of her Resemblance to a Garden. Wrote by her servant, V. B.'

> (*The beauty of this makes her falter. She looks up.*)

VALENTINE (*with a poet's pride*). There is more of it, ma'am.

PHOEBE (*reading*)

> The lilies are her pretty thoughts,
>   Her shoulders are the may,
> Her smiles are all forget-me-nots,
>   The path 's her gracious way,

The roses that do line it are
     Her fancies walking round,
'Tis sweetly smelling lavender
     In which my lady's gowned.

(MISS PHOEBE *has thought herself strong,
but she is not able to read such exquisite
lines without betraying herself to a lover's
gaze.*)

VALENTINE (*excitedly*).   Miss Phoebe, when
did you cease to care for me?

PHOEBE (*retreating from him but clinging to her
poem*).   You promised not to ask.

VALENTINE.   I know not why you should,
Miss Phoebe, but I believe you love me still!

(MISS PHOEBE *has the terrified appearance
of a detected felon.*)

(MISS SUSAN *returns.*)

MISS SUSAN.   You are talking so loudly.

VALENTINE.   Miss Susan, does she care for me
still?

MISS SUSAN (*forgetting her pride of sex*).   Oh,
sir, how could she help it.

VALENTINE.   Then by Gad, Miss Phoebe, you

shall marry me though I have to carry you in my arms to the church.

PHOEBE. Sir, how can you!

> (*But* MISS SUSAN *gives her a look which means that it must be done if only to avoid such a scandal. It is at this inopportune moment that* MISS HENRIETTA *and* MISS FANNY *are announced.*)

MISS HENRIETTA. I think Miss Willoughby has already popped in.

PHOEBE (*with a little spirit*). Yes, indeed.

MISS SUSAN (*a mistress of sarcasm*). How is Mary, Fanny? She has not been to see us for several minutes.

MISS FANNY (*somewhat daunted*). Mary is so partial to you, Susan.

VALENTINE. Your servant, Miss Henrietta, Miss Fanny.

MISS FANNY. How do you do, sir?

MISS HENRIETTA (*wistfully*). And how do you find Miss Livvy, sir?

VALENTINE. I have not seen her, Miss Henrietta.

MISS HENRIETTA. Indeed!

MISS FANNY. Not even you?

VALENTINE. You seem surprised?

MISS FANNY. Nay, sir, you must not say so; but really, Phoebe!

PHOEBE. Fanny, you presume!

VALENTINE (*puzzled*). If one of you ladies would deign to enlighten me. To begin with, what is Miss Livvy's malady?

MISS HENRIETTA. He does not know? Oh, Phoebe.

VALENTINE. Ladies, have pity on a dull man, and explain.

MISS FANNY (*timidly*). Please not to ask us to explain. I fear we have already said more than was proper. Phoebe, forgive.

> (*To* CAPTAIN BROWN *this but adds to the mystery, and he looks to* PHOEBE *for enlightenment.*)

PHOEBE (*desperate*). I understand, sir, there is a belief that I keep Livvy in confinement because of your passion for her.

VALENTINE. My passion for Miss Livvy? Why, Miss Fanny, I cannot abide her—nor she me. (*Looking manfully at* MISS PHOEBE.)

Furthermore, I am proud to tell you that this is the lady whom I adore.

MISS FANNY.   Phoebe?

VALENTINE.   Yes, ma'am.

> (*The ladies are for a moment bereft of speech, and the uplifted* PHOEBE *cannot refrain from a movement which, if completed, would be a curtsy. Her punishment follows promptly.*)

MISS HENRIETTA (*from her heart*).   Phoebe, I am so happy 'tis you.

MISS FANNY.   Dear Phoebe, I give you joy. And you also, sir.   (MISS PHOEBE *sends her sister a glance of unutterable woe, and escapes from the room.   It is most ill-bred of her.*)   Miss Susan, I do not understand !

MISS HENRIETTA.   Is it that Miss Livvy is an obstacle?

MISS SUSAN (*who knows that there is no hope for her but in flight*).   I think I hear Phoebe calling me—a sudden indisposition.   Pray excuse me, Henrietta.   (*She goes.*)

MISS HENRIETTA.   We know not, sir, whether to offer you our felicitations?

VALENTINE (*cogitating*).   May I ask, ma'am, what you mean by an obstacle?   Is there some mystery about Miss Livvy?

MISS HENRIETTA.   So much so, sir, that we at one time thought she and Miss Phoebe were the same person.

VALENTINE.   Pshaw!

MISS FANNY.   Why will they admit no physician into her presence?

MISS HENRIETTA.   The blinds of her room are kept most artfully drawn.

MISS FANNY (*plaintively*).   We have never seen her, sir.   Neither Miss Susan nor Miss Phoebe will present her to us.

VALENTINE (*impressed*).   Indeed.

> (MISS HENRIETTA *and* MISS FANNY, *encouraged by his sympathy, draw nearer the door of the interesting bedchamber.   They falter.   Any one who thinks, however, that they would so far forget themselves as to open the door and peep in, has no understanding of the ladies of Quality Street.   They are, nevertheless, not perfect, for* MISS HENRIETTA *knocks on the door.*)

MISS HENRIETTA. How do you find yourself, dear Miss Livvy?

> (*There is no answer. It is our pride to record that they come away without even touching the handle. They look appealing at* CAPTAIN BROWN, *whose face has grown grave.*)

VALENTINE. I think, ladies, as a physician——

> (*He walks into the bedroom. They feel an ignoble drawing to follow him, but do not yield to it. When he returns his face is inscrutable.*)

MISS HENRIETTA. Is she very poorly, sir?

VALENTINE. Ha.

MISS FANNY. We did not hear you address her.

VALENTINE. She is not awake, ma'am.

MISS HENRIETTA. It is provoking.

MISS FANNY (*sternly just*). They informed Mary that she was nigh asleep.

VALENTINE. It is not a serious illness I think, ma'am. With the permission of Miss Phoebe and Miss Susan I will make myself more acquaint with her disorder presently. (*He is desirous to be alone.*)   But we must not talk lest we disturb her.

MISS FANNY.   You suggest our retiring, sir?

VALENTINE.   Nay, Miss Fanny——

MISS FANNY.   You are very obliging; but I think, Henrietta——

MISS HENRIETTA (*rising*).   Yes, Fanny.

> (*No doubt th y are the more ready to depart that they wish to inform* MISS WILLOUGHBY *at once of these strange doings. As they go,* MISS SUSAN *and* MISS PHOEBE *return, and the adieux are less elaborate than usual. Neither visitors nor hostesses quite know what to say.* MISS SUSAN *is merely relieved to see them leave, but* MISS PHOEBE *has read something in their manner that makes her uneasy.*)

PHOEBE.   Why have they departed so hurriedly, sir? They—they did not go in to see Livvy?

VALENTINE.   No.

> (*She reads danger in his face.*)

PHOEBE. Why do you look at me so strangely?

VALENTINE (*somewhat stern*). Miss Phoebe, I desire to see Miss Livvy.

PHOEBE. Impossible.

VALENTINE. Why impossible? They tell me strange stories about no one's seeing her. Miss Phoebe, I will not leave this house until I have seen her.

PHOEBE. You cannot. (*But he is very determined, and she is afraid of him.*) Will you excuse me, sir, while I talk with Susan behind the door?

> (*The sisters go guiltily into the bedroom, and* CAPTAIN BROWN *after some hesitation rings for* PATTY.)

VALENTINE. Patty, come here. Why is this trick being played upon me?

PATTY (*with all her wits about her*). Trick, sir! Who would dare?

VALENTINE. I know, Patty, that Miss Phoebe has been Miss Livvy all the time.

PATTY. I give in!

VALENTINE. Why has she done this?

PATTY (*beseechingly*). Are you laughing, sir?

VALENTINE. I am very far from laughing.

PATTY (*turning on him*). 'Twas you that began it, all by not knowing her in the white gown.

VALENTINE. Why has this deception been kept up so long?

PATTY. Because you would not see through it. Oh, the wicked denseness. She thought you were infatuate with Miss Livvy because she was young and silly.

VALENTINE. It is infamous.

PATTY. I will not have you call her names. 'Twas all playful innocence at first, and now she is so feared of you she is weeping her soul to death, and all I do I cannot rouse her. 'I ha' a follower in the kitchen, ma'am,' says I, to infuriate her. 'Give him a glass of cowslip wine,' says she, like a gentle lamb. And ill she can afford it, you having lost their money for them.

VALENTINE. What is that? On the contrary, all the money they have, Patty, they owe to my having invested it for them.

PATTY. That is the money they lost.

VALENTINE. You are sure of that?

PATTY.   I can swear to it.

VALENTINE.   Deceived me about that also. Good God; but why?

PATTY.   I think she was feared you would offer to her out of pity.   She said something to Miss Susan about keeping a flag flying.   What she meant I know not.   (*But he knows, and he turns away his face.*)   Are you laughing, sir?

VALENTINE.   No, Patty, I am not laughing. Why do they not say Miss Livvy has gone home? It would save them a world of trouble.

PATTY.   The Misses Willoughby and Miss Henrietta—they watch the house all day.   They would say she cannot be gone, for we did not see her go.

VALENTINE (*enlightened at last*).   I see!

PATTY.   And Miss Phoebe and Miss Susan wring their hands, for they are feared Miss Livvy is bedridden here for all time.   (*Now his sense of humour asserts itself*).   Thank the Lord, you 're laughing!

> (*At this he laughs the more, and it is a gay* CAPTAIN BROWN *on whom* MISS SUSAN *opens the bedroom door.   This desperate*

*woman is too full of plot to note the change
in him.*)

MISS SUSAN.   I am happy to inform you, sir,
that Livvy finds herself much improved.

VALENTINE (*bowing*).   It is joy to me to hear
it.

MISS SUSAN.   She is coming in to see you.

PATTY (*aghast*).   Oh, ma'am!

VALENTINE (*frowning on* PATTY).   I shall be
happy to see the poor invalid.

PATTY.   Ma'am——!

> (*But* MISS SUSAN, *believing that so far all
> is well, has returned to the bedchamber.*
> CAPTAIN BROWN *bestows a quizzical glance
> upon the maid.*)

VALENTINE.   Go away, Patty.   Anon I may
claim a service of you, but for the present, go.

PATTY.   But—but——

VALENTINE.   Retire, woman.

> (*She has to go, and he prepares his face for
> the reception of the invalid.* PHOEBE
> comes in without her cap, the ringlets
> showing again. She wears a dressing
> jacket and is supported by* MISS SUSAN.)

VALENTINE (*gravely*). Your servant, Miss Livvy.

PHOEBE (*weakly*). How do you do?

VALENTINE. Allow me, Miss Susan.

> (*He takes* MISS SUSAN's *place; but after an exquisite moment* MISS PHOEBE *breaks away from him, feeling that she is not worthy of such bliss.*)

PHOEBE. No, no, I—I can walk alone—see. (*She reclines upon the couch.*)

MISS SUSAN. How do you think she is looking?

> (*He makes a professional examination of the patient, and they are very ashamed to deceive him, but not so ashamed that they must confess.*)

What do you think?

VALENTINE (*solemnly*). She will recover. May I say, ma'am, it surprises me that any one should see much resemblance between you and your Aunt Phoebe. Miss Phoebe is decidedly shorter and more thick-set.

PHOEBE (*sitting up*). No, I am not.

VALENTINE. I said Miss Phoebe, ma'am.

(*She reclines.*) But tell me, is not Miss Phoebe to join us?

PHOEBE. She hopes you will excuse her, sir.

MISS SUSAN (*vaguely*). Taking the opportunity of airing the room.

VALENTINE. Ah, of course.

MISS SUSAN (*opening bedroom door and calling mendaciously*). Captain Brown will excuse you, Phoebe.

VALENTINE. Certainly, Miss Susan. Well, ma'am, I think I could cure Miss Livvy if she is put unreservedly into my hands.

MISS SUSAN (*with a sigh*). I am sure you could.

VALENTINE. Then you are my patient, Miss Livvy.

PHOEBE (*nervously*). 'Twas but a passing indisposition, I am almost quite recovered.

VALENTINE. Nay, you still require attention. Do you propose making a long stay in Quality Street, ma'am?

PHOEBE. I—I—I hope not. It—it depends.

MISS SUSAN (*forgetting herself*). Mary is the worst.

VALENTINE. I ask your pardon?

PHOEBE.   Aunt Susan, you are excited.

VALENTINE.   But you are quite right, Miss Livvy; home is the place for you.

PHOEBE.   Would that I could go!

VALENTINE.   You are going.

PHOEBE.   Yes—soon.

VALENTINE.   Indeed, I have a delightful surprise for you, Miss Livvy, you are going to-day.

PHOEBE.   To-day?

VALENTINE.   Not merely to-day, but now. As it happens, my carriage is standing idle at your door, and I am to take you in it to your home—some twenty miles if I remember.

PHOEBE.   You are to take me?

VALENTINE.   Nay, 'tis no trouble at all, and as your physician my mind is made up.   Some wraps for her, Miss Susan.

MISS SUSAN.   But—but——

PHOEBE (*in a panic*).   Sir, I decline to go.

VALENTINE.   Come, Miss Livvy, you are in my hands.

PHOEBE.   I decline.   I am most determined.

VALENTINE.   You admit yourself that you are recovered.

PHOEBE. I do not feel so well now. Aunt Susan !

MISS SUSAN. Sir——

VALENTINE. If you wish to consult Miss Phoebe——

MISS SUSAN. Oh, no.

VALENTINE. Then the wraps, Miss Susan.

PHOEBE. Auntie, don't leave me.

VALENTINE. What a refractory patient it is. But reason with her, Miss Susan, and I shall ask Miss Phoebe for some wraps.

PHOEBE. Sir !

> (*To their consternation he goes cheerily into the bedroom.* MISS PHOEBE *saves herself by instant flight, and nothing but mesmeric influence keeps* MISS SUSAN *rooted to the blue and white room. When he returns he is loaded with wraps, and still cheerfully animated, as if he had found nothing untoward in* LIVVY's *bed-chamber.*)

VALENTINE. I think these will do admirably, Miss Susan.

MISS SUSAN. But Phoebe——

VALENTINE. If I swathe Miss Livvy in these——

MISS SUSAN. Phoebe——

VALENTINE. She is still busy airing the room. (*The extraordinary man goes to the couch as if unable to perceive that its late occupant has gone, and* MISS SUSAN *watches him, fascinated.*) Come, Miss Livvy, put these over you. Allow me— this one over your shoulders, so. Be so obliging as to lean on me. Be brave, ma'am, you cannot fall—my arm is round you; gently, gently, Miss Livvy; ah, that is better; we are doing famously; come, come. Good-bye, Miss Susan, I will take every care of her.

> (*He has gone, with the bundle on his arm, but* MISS SUSAN *does not wake up. Even the banging of the outer door is unable to rouse her. It is heard, however, by* MISS PHOEBE, *who steals back into the room, her cap upon her head to give her courage.*)

PHOEBE. He is gone! (MISS SUSAN'S *rapt face alarms her.*) Oh, Susan, was he as dreadful as that?

MISS SUSAN (*in tones unnatural to her*). Phoebe, he knows all.

PHOEBE.   Yes, of course he knows all now. Sister, did his face change? Oh, Susan, what did he say?

MISS SUSAN.   He said 'Good-bye, Miss Susan.' That was almost all he said.

PHOEBE.   Did his eyes flash fire?

MISS SUSAN. Phoebe, it was what he did. He—he took Livvy with him.

PHOEBE.   Susan, dear, don't say that. You are not distraught, are you?

MISS SUSAN (*clinging to facts*). He did; he wrapped her up in a shawl.

PHOEBE.   Susan! You are Susan Throssel, my love. You remember me, don't you? Phoebe, your sister. I was Livvy also, you know, Livvy.

MISS SUSAN.   He took Livvy with him.

PHOEBE (*in woe*). Oh, oh! sister, who am I?

MISS SUSAN.   You are Phoebe.

PHOEBE.   And who was Livvy?

MISS SUSAN.   You were.

PHOEBE. Thank heaven.

MISS SUSAN. But he took her away in the carriage.

PHOEBE. Oh, dear! (*She has quite forgotten her own troubles now.*) Susan, you will soon be well again. Dear, let us occupy our minds. Shall we draw up the advertisement for the reopening of the school?

MISS SUSAN. I do so hate the school.

PHOEBE. Come, dear, come, sit down. Write, Susan. (*Dictating.*) 'The Misses Throssel have the pleasure to announce——'

MISS SUSAN. Pleasure! Oh, Phoebe.

PHOEBE. 'That they will resume school on the 5th of next month. Music, embroidery, the backboard, and all the elegancies of the mind. Latin—shall we say algebra?'

MISS SUSAN. I refuse to write algebra.

PHOEBE. —for beginners.

MISS SUSAN. I refuse. There is only one thing I can write; it writes itself in my head all day. 'Miss Susan Throssel presents her compliments to the Misses Willoughby and Miss Henrietta Turnbull, and requests the honour of their presence at the nuptials of her sister Phoebe and Captain Valentine Brown.'

PHOEBE. Susan!

MISS SUSAN. Phoebe! (*A door is heard banging.*) He has returned!

PHOEBE. Oh cruel, cruel. Susan, I am so alarmed.

MISS SUSAN. I will face him.

PHOEBE. Nay, if it must be, I will.

(*But when he enters he is not very terrible.*)

VALENTINE. Miss Phoebe, it is not raining, but your face is wet. I wish always to kiss you when your face is wet.

PHOEBE. Susan!

VALENTINE. Miss Livvy will never trouble you any more, Miss Susan. I have sent her home.

MISS SUSAN. Oh, sir, how can you invent such a story for us.

VALENTINE. I did not. I invented it for the Misses Willoughby and Miss Henrietta, who from their windows watched me put her into my carriage. Patty accompanies her, and in a few hours Patty will return alone.

MISS SUSAN. Phoebe, he has got rid of Livvy!

PHOEBE. Susan, his face hasn't changed!

VALENTINE. Dear Phoebe Throssel, will you be Phoebe Brown?

PHOEBE (*quivering*). You know everything? And that I am not a garden?

VALENTINE. I know everything, ma'am— except that.

PHOEBE (*so very glad to be prim at the end*). Sir, the dictates of my heart enjoin me to accept your too flattering offer. (*He puts her cap in his pocket. He kisses her.* MISS SUSAN *is about to steal away.*) Oh, sir, Susan also. (*He kisses* MISS SUSAN *also; and here we bid them good-bye.*)

The End.

JAN 1 6 1953

FEB 3 1972